The MIRACLE MORNING

for COLLEGE STUDENTS

COMPANION PLANNER

Hal Elrod • Natalie Janji

With Honorée Corder

THE MIRACLE MORNING FOR COLLEGE STUDENTS PLANNER

Hal Elrod & Natalie Janji
with Honorée Corder

Interior Design: Christina Culbertson, 3CsBooks.com

Paperback ISBN-978-1-942589-19-8
Digital ISBN: 978-1-942589-20-4

This planner belongs to:

_____

If lost please return to:

_____

_____

_____

Contact Information

_____

_____

DEDICATION

NATALIE

This book is dedicated to my brother. George, you were the first to teach me how to prioritize and organize my time. You inspire me by the way you live your life. I am so grateful to have a brother like you. Thank you, and I love you!

INTRODUCTION

In 2012, Hal published *The Miracle Morning: The Not-So-Obvious Secret Guaranteed To Transform Your Life Before 8AM.* In this book, that has since become an international bestseller, Hal introduced us to the Life S.A.V.E.R.S., and has changed the lives of millions of people all around the world. After the enormous amount of success, Hal and Honorée Corder have produced The Miracle Morning Book Series, which extended *The Miracle Morning* to create titles such as *The Miracle Morning for Real Estate Agents, The Miracle Morning for Network Marketers, The Miracle Morning for Salespeople, The Miracle Morning for Parents and Families, The Miracle Morning Art of Affirmations, The Miracle Morning for Writers, The Miracle Morning for Entrepreneurs,* and *The Miracle Morning for Transforming Your Relationship,* among others.

In May 2017, Hal, Honorée and I created **The Miracle Morning for College Students.** Using this book, students have begun implementing the Life S.A.V.E.R.S. in their lives and witnessing every area of their lives changing for the better. They have learned why mornings matter more than they think, how to master their own self-leadership and personal growth, how to manage their *energy* – physical, mental, and emotional – and how to apply their new skills to their academics, their social life, their health, and their plans for post-graduation and career. Through their work with the book, students have begun feeling hope for their future and have taken 100% responsibility for their dreams and their goals.

Now, we present **The Miracle Morning for College Students Companion Planner.** This planner will be the tool you need to implement the Life S.A.V.E.R.S. in your life and create the foundational schedule that will strengthen your self-leadership skills to build a better you. It will guide you to identify your priorities, break up larger tasks into many smaller tasks, organize your life, manage your time, and time-block to accomplish your goals. This planner furthers the mission of *The Miracle Morning for*

College Students: to increase self-awareness, self-leadership, and to help students create productive habits in skills such as their academics, social life, health and preparation for post-graduation.

Before we go into how to use this planner, let's review the life-changing concept of the Life S.A.V.E.R.S. and how you can implement it in your life as students.

The Life S.A.V.E.R.S. is a compilation of six habits that have been practiced over centuries.

"S" IS FOR SILENCE

Starting each day with a period of silence instead of looking at your phone or starting your busy day will immediately reduce your stress levels and help you begin the day with the calm and clarity that you need to focus on what's most important. You have a number of choices for your practice of silence. In no particular order, here are a few to get you started:

- Meditation
- Prayer
- Reflection
- Deep breathing
- Gratitude

Silence in the form of meditation reduces stress and, as a result, improves your health. A major study run by several groups, including the National Institutes of Health, the American Medical Association, the Mayo Clinic, and scientists from both Harvard and Stanford, revealed that meditation reduces stress and high blood pressure. A recent study by Dr. Norman Rosenthal, a world-renowned psychiatrist who works with the David Lynch Foundation, even found that people who practice meditation are 30 percent less likely to die from heart disease.

Meditation helps you to slow down and focus on you, even if it's for just a short time. Start your meditation practice and say goodbye to feeling scattered and wandering aimlessly without intention and purpose through your day.

Meditation is like anything else: if you've never done it before, it can be difficult or feel awkward at first. If you are a first-time meditator, I recommend starting with a guided meditation. A list of meditation apps is available in the Resources section in the back of the planner.

Think of daily meditation as a temporary vacation from the challenges of life. Although your problems will still be there when you finish each day, you'll find that you're more centered and better equipped to solve them.

"A" IS FOR AFFIRMATIONS

Reciting affirmations is a practice to strengthen your mindset. Mindset is the accumulation of your beliefs, attitude, and emotional intelligence. In her bestselling book, *Mindset: The New Psychology of Success*, Carol Dweck, Ph.D., explains it this way: "For twenty years, my research has shown that the view you adopt of yourself profoundly affects the way you lead your life."

Science has proven that affirmations are one of the most effective tools for quickly becoming the person you need to be to achieve everything you want in your life—for yourself, your academics, and your relationships.

Reciting affirmations is a tool to enable you to become more intentional about your goals while also providing the encouragement and positive mindset necessary to achieve them.

By repeatedly articulating and reinforcing to yourself *what* result you want to accomplish, *why* accomplishing it is important to you, *which* specific actions are required to produce that result, and, most importantly, precisely *when* you commit to taking those actions, your subconscious mind will shift your beliefs and behavior. You'll begin to believe your affirmations and behave in new ways, and eventually manifest your affirmations into your reality.

"V" IS FOR VISUALIZATION

Visualization has long been a well-known practice of world-class athletes, who use it to optimize their performance. Olympic athletes and top performers in many sports incorporate visualization as a critical part of their daily training. What is less well known is that the top achievers among successful entrepreneurs use it just as frequently.

Visualization is a technique by which you use your imagination to create a compelling picture of your future, providing you with heightened clarity and producing the motivation that will assist you in making your vision a reality.

Most people are limited by visions of their past results. They replay previous failures and heartbreaks. Creative visualization, however, enables you to *design* the vision that will occupy your mind, ensuring that the greatest pull on you is your future—a compelling, exciting, and limitless future. The perfect time to visualize yourself living in alignment with your affirmations is right after you read them.

Many people don't feel comfortable visualizing success and are even scared to succeed. They may experience resistance to this practice. Some may even feel guilty that they will leave colleagues, friends, and family members behind when they become successful. The greatest gift you can give to those you love and those you lead is to live to your full potential. What does that look like for you?

There is scientific evidence showing that merely visualizing the result you want (e.g., the new car, the dream house, crossing the finish line, standing on stage, etc.) can actually diminish your drive because your brain has already experienced the reward on some level. Instead, focus your visualization on the necessary actions. Visualize yourself performing the actions—especially those that you habitually resist and procrastinate on—in a way that creates a compelling mental and emotional experience of the action.

You might picture yourself enjoying getting your work done. Spend time imagining yourself studying for an exam, for example. What does it look like? How does it feel as you remain focused and understand the concepts? Picture yourself responding to obstacles and issues with ease.

If writing papers is a chore for you, you can visualize yourself calmly outlining your paper. Imagine that you are excited to work on your paper for the freedom waiting for you after it is finished!

You can pick anything that is a critical action step or skill that you may not be performing at your best yet. Envisioning success and what it takes to get there will prepare you for, and almost ensure, a successful day.

"E" IS FOR EXERCISE

Exercise should be a staple of your Miracle Morning. Even a few minutes of exercise each day significantly enhances your health, improves your self-confidence and emotional well-being, and enables you to think better and concentrate longer. You'll also notice how quickly your energy increases with daily exercise, and the people you spend the most time with will notice it too.

You can go for a walk or run, follow along to a yoga video on YouTube, or find a Life S.A.V.E.R.S. buddy and play some early morning racquetball. There's also an excellent app called 7 Minute Workout that gives you a full body workout in—you guessed it—seven minutes. The choice is yours, but pick one activity and do it.

As a college student you are constantly on the go. You need an endless reserve of energy to make the best of the challenges that come your way, and a daily morning exercise practice is going to provide it.

If you want to maintain good health and increase your energy, you must exercise consistently. That's not news to anyone, and it is easy to make excuses. Two of the biggest are "I don't have time" and "I'm too tired." And those are just the first two on the list. There is no limit to the excuses you can think of. And the more creative you are, the more excuses you can find!

That's the beauty of incorporating exercise into your Miracle Morning—it happens before your day wears you out and before you've had hours to come up with new excuses. Because it comes first, the Miracle Morning is a surefire way to avoid those stumbling blocks and make exercise a daily habit.

Legal disclaimer: You should consult your physician before beginning any exercise regimen, especially if you are experiencing any physical pain, discomfort, disabilities, etc. You may need to modify or even refrain from an exercise routine to meet your individual needs.

"R" IS FOR READING

One of the fastest ways to achieve everything you want is to find successful people to be your role models. For every goal you have, there's a good chance an expert out there has already achieved the same thing or something similar. As Tony Robbins says, "success leaves clues."

Fortunately, some of the best of the best have shared their stories in writing. And that means all those success blueprints are just waiting for anyone willing to invest the time in reading. Books are a limitless supply of help and mentorship right at your fingertips.

In addition to finding confidence as a student, you can transform your relationships, increase your self-esteem, improve your communication skills, learn how to become healthy, and improve any other area of your life you can think of. Head to your library or local bookstore—or do what I do and visit Amazon.com—and you'll find more books than you can possibly imagine on any area of your life you want to improve.

I recommend making a commitment to read a minimum of ten pages per day (although five is okay to start with if you read slowly or don't yet enjoy reading). Ten pages may not seem like a lot, but let's do the math. Reading ten pages a day adds up to 3,650 pages per year, which stacks up to approximately eighteen 200-page books that will enable you to take yourself to the next level so that you can take your success in your academic and professional life to the next level. All in just 10–15 minutes of daily reading, or 15–30 minutes if you read more slowly.

"S" IS FOR SCRIBING

Scribing is simply another word for writing. The scribing element of your Miracle Morning enables you to write down what you're grateful for, as well as document your insights, ideas, breakthroughs, realizations, successes, and lessons learned, including any areas of opportunity, personal growth, or improvement.

Most Miracle Morning practitioners scribe in a journal for five to ten minutes during their Miracle Morning. By getting your thoughts out of your head and putting them in writing, you'll immediately gain heightened awareness, clarity, and valuable insights that you'd otherwise forget or be oblivious to.

Writing will give you the daily benefit of consciously directing your thoughts, but what's even more powerful are the insights you'll gain from reviewing your journals, from cover to cover, afterwards—especially at the end of the year. As Tony Robbins has said many times, "A life worth living is a life worth recording."

Here are three simple steps to get started with journaling or improve your current journaling process.

1. Choose a format: physical or digital. You'll want to decide up front if you prefer a traditional, physical journal or a digital journal (on your computer or an app for your mobile device). If you aren't sure, experiment with both and see which feels best.

2. Obtain the journal of your choice. Almost anything can work, but when it comes to a physical journal, there is something to be said for a durable one that you enjoy looking at—after all, ideally you're going to have it for the rest of your life. I like to buy high quality leather journals with lines on the pages, but it's your journal, so choose what works best for you. Some people prefer journals without lines so they can draw or create mind maps. Others like to have a predated book with a page for each day of the year to help them stay accountable.

3. Scribe daily. You'll find endless things you can write about—notes from the book you're reading, a list of things you're grateful for, and your top three to five priorities for the day are good items to start with. Write whatever makes you feel good and helps you optimize your day. Don't worry about grammar, spelling, or punctuation. Your journal is a place to let your imagination run wild, so keep a muzzle on your inner critic and don't edit—just scribe!

For more information about each of the practices in the Life S.A.V.E.R.S., such as recommended books to read, sample affirmations, or sample journal questions, visit the References section in the back of this planner.

You may have heard the phrase "Knowledge is Power," but it's not accurate. It is the *implementation* of knowledge that is power. The Life S.A.V.E.R.S. changed my life. It was not because I read *The Miracle Morning* book many times, but because I implemented these habits in my daily routine. This is why we created this planner for you. This planner will allow you to reinforce the knowledge you learned in *The Miracle Morning for College Students.* You will be able to accomplish your dreams and goals by practicing the Life S.A.V.E.R.S., having a written plan with dates and deadlines, and becoming aware of the steps you can take to improve every area of your life.

The Miracle Morning for College Students Companion Planner

This companion guide to *The Miracle Morning for College Students* will allow you to strengthen the positive habits you are developing that will carry you far beyond your years of college. Here is an overview of pages included in this planner:

- *Dreams-* Identify and write out your dreams

- *Vision Board-* Paste or draw pictures to create a visual representation of your dreams and goals that will travel with you everywhere you take this planner

- *Monthly Overview-* Write out your monthly goal(s), important events, projects with their deadlines for the entire month. You will also be able to write a reminder of the important dates that need to be transferred to your phone calendar, and also brainstorm any ideas that you have during the month

- *Monthly Reflection-* Answer questions to reflect upon your last month and focus on how to achieve in the next month

- *Weekly Overview-* Write out your weekly goal, action you took for each habit in the Life S.A.V.E.R.S., intention for the day, and daily gratitude. You will also be able to set your foundational schedule from 6:00am-11:30pm. Lastly, you'll be able to check off the items you need to have ready for the next day of Life S.A.V.E.R.S., classes, and other responsibilities

- *Weekly Reflection-* Answer questions to reflect on the past week and evaluate the steps you will take to improve for the next week

- *References-* This section has many resources including:

  - U.S. Map with capitols of states and Time Zones

  - Meditation Apps

  - Sample College Student Affirmations

  - List of Recommended Books

  - Sample Journal Questions

  - Conversion Table

In the following pages, you will see a few samples about how you might use this planner.

Remember, this planner is *yours*. With this planner, you can design the Level 10 life you want to live. You are more than capable, worthy, and deserving of living your Level 10 vision. As I said in *The Miracle Morning for College Students,* "What isn't the future going to hold for you?!" Practice the Life S.A.V.E.R.S. and watch your life transform right in front of your eyes. Be BOLD in the pursuit toward your vision!

Happy Planning!

MONTH OF: May	SUNDAY	MONDAY	TUESDAY
This Month's Goal Finish all projects & Ace those finals!		1	2 Bio Quiz
	7	8	9 Biology Project Due
Important Events or Reminders to Transfer to My Phone 1. Biology test 2. Babysitting Thursdays 3. Finish Lab by 5/29 4. Outline Speech 5. 6. 7. 8. 9. 10.	14	15 NO class !	16
	21 Family Dinner	22	23 Midterm paper
	28 Email reading log	29 Ethics Exam	30 Draft Due Today!

PROJECT NAME	CLASS & INSTRUCTOR	IMPORTANT DATES	DEADLINES
1. Speech Presentation	Speech – Rogers	May 28th Reading	Outline May 5th Draft May 30th
2. Biology Lab	Bio 101 – Smith	Quiz 5/2	Project May 9th Labs May 25th
3. Finish Lab Assignments	Calculus – Ronald	Exam May 17th	Labs Due May 25th
4. Midterm paper	Ethics – Brown	Exam May 29th	Paper May 23rd

WEDNESDAY	THURSDAY	FRIDAY	SATURDAY
3	4 Jessica's Birthday	5 Outline Due ****	6 Movies with friends
10	11 Babysitting Riley's 6pm	12 Trip to NY	13
17 Calculus Exam	18 Babysitting Riley's 5pm	19 Honor's Luncheon 12pm	20 Volunteering at animal shelter
24	25 Turn in labs Babysitting Riley's 6pm	26	John's Bday 27
31 Register for fall classes			

BRAINSTORM

Prosperity
Giving back and helping others- pick up leaves & volunteering

Planning ———————— Work

↓

SUCCESS

- Save up for new bike
- Regsiter for Fall
- Tutoring with April
- A in Biology

Week of:	Sunday	Monday	Tuesday
This Week's Goal	S 10-min meditation ✓	S 10-min meditation ✓	S 10-min meditation ✓
	A Recited them ✓	A Wrote them ✓	A Recited them ✓
Complete SAVERS &	V Pictured studying ✓	V Pictured speaking ✓	V Pictured studying ✓
assignments due next	E Pushups/Jumping jacks ✓	E 30 min jogging ✓	E 30 min Gym ✓
week	R 15 pages TMM4CS ✓	R 20 pages TMM ✓	R 15 pages TMM ✓
	S Journaling ✓	S Reflect on reading ✓	S Journaling ✓
Intention for the Day	◆ Prosperity	◆ Lead by example	◆ Happiness
Grateful for ...	◆ Friends	◆ My health	◆ Laughter

> *No matter what people tell you, words and ideas can change the world.*
>
> **—ROBIN WILLIAMS**

TO-DO LIST

Highest Priority

Finish Lab Assignments

Definite Priority

Reading for Lit

Lowest Priority

Clean bathroom

Habit to Work on This Week

Daily healthy breakfast

Time	Sunday	Monday	Tuesday
5:00			
5:30			
6:00			
6:30			
7:00			
7:30			
8:00		Class	
8:30			
9:00			Tutoring
9:30			
10:00			
10:30			
11:00			
11:30		Finish Assignments	
12:00			
12:30			
1:00		Class	Class
1:30			
2:00	Study		
2:30			
3:00	Finish Assignments		
3:30			
4:00			
4:30			
5:00			
5:30	Work		
6:00			Work
6:30			
7:00			
7:30			
8:00			
8:30		Study	
9:00			
9:30			
10:00		Bed	
10:30	Bed		Bed
11:00			

Ready for tomorrow?	(✓)	(✓)	(✓)
ALARM	6:30 am ✓	6:00 am ✓	6:00 am ✓
CLOTHES/BACKPACK		Dress up ✓	✓
GLASS OF WATER	✓	✓	✓
SAVERS PREP			
BEDTIME AFFIRMATIONS	Wrote them ✓	Recited them ✓	Wrote them ✓

Wednesday	Thursday	Friday	Saturday
S 10-min meditation ✓	S 10-min meditation ✓	S 10-min meditation ✓	S 10-min meditation ✓
A Recited them ✓	A Wrote them ✓	A Recited them ✓	A Wrote them ✓
V Pictured test-taking ✓	V Pictured studying ✓	V Pictured test-taking ✓	V Pictured studying ✓
E Pushups/Jumping jacks ✓	E 30 min jogging ✓	E Pushups/Jumping jacks ✓	E 30 min jogging ✓
R 15 pages TMMCS ✓	R 18 pages TMMCS ✓	R 15 pages TMMCS ✓	R 18 pages TMMCS ✓
S Reflect on reading ✓	S Journaling	S Reflect on reading ✓	S Journaling
◆ Help a stranger	◆ Forgiveness	◆ Lead by example	◆ Prosperity
◆ My mom	◆ Family time	◆ Laughter	◆ My health

Time	Wednesday	Thursday	Friday	Saturday
5:00				
5:30				
6:00				
6:30				
7:00				
7:30				
8:00	Class		Class	
8:30				
9:00		Tutoring		
9:30				
10:00				Study
10:30				
11:00				
11:30	Finish Assignments		Study	
12:00				
12:30				
1:00	Class	Class	Class	
1:30				
2:00				Finish Assignments
2:30				
3:00				
3:30				
4:00				
4:30				
5:00				
5:30		Work	Work	
6:00				
6:30				Go out with friends
7:00				
7:30	Study			
8:00				
8:30				
9:00				
9:30				
10:00	Bed			
10:30		Bed		
11:00			Bed	Bed

(✓)	(✓)	(✓)	(✓)
6:00 am ✓	6:00 am ✓	6:00 am ✓	6:30 am ✓
Extra notepad ✓	Dress up ✓	Dress up ✓	Study notes ✓
✓	✓	✓	✓
Recited them ✓	Wrote them ✓	Recited them ✓	Recited them ✓

Love the life you have while you create the life of your dreams. Don't think you have to choose one over the other.

—HAL ELROD

DREAMS

· ·

Write out your dreams below ...

VISION BOARD

Paste or draw pictures of your visions ...

MONTH OF:	SUNDAY	MONDAY	TUESDAY
This Month's Goal			
Important Events or Reminders to Transfer to My Phone			
1.			
2.			
3.			
4.			
5.			
6.			
7.			
8.			
9.			
10.			

PROJECT NAME	CLASS & INSTRUCTOR	IMPORTANT DATES	DEADLINES
1.			
2.			
3.			
4.			

WEDNESDAY	THURSDAY	FRIDAY	SATURDAY

BRAINSTORM

Week of:	Sunday	Monday	Tuesday
This Week's Goal	S	S	S
	A	A	A
	V	V	V
	E	E	E
	R	R	R
	S	S	S
Intention for the Day	◆	◆	◆
Grateful for ...	◆	◆	◆

No matter what people tell you, words and ideas can change the world.

–ROBIN WILLIAMS

TO-DO LIST

Highest Priority

Definite Priority

Lowest Priority

Habit to Work on This Week

Time	Sunday	Monday	Tuesday
5:00		5:00	5:00
5:30		5:30	5:30
6:00		6:00	6:00
6:30		6:30	6:30
7:00		7:00	7:00
7:30		7:30	7:30
8:00		8:00	8:00
8:30		8:30	8:30
9:00		9:00	9:00
9:30		9:30	9:30
10:00		10:00	10:00
10:30		10:30	10:30
11:00		11:00	11:00
11:30		11:30	11:30
12:00		12:00	12:00
12:30		12:30	12:30
1:00		1:00	1:00
1:30		1:30	1:30
2:00		2:00	2:00
2:30		2:30	2:30
3:00		3:00	3:00
3:30		3:30	3:30
4:00		4:00	4:00
4:30		4:30	4:30
5:00		5:00	5:00
5:30		5:30	5:30
6:00		6:00	6:00
6:30		6:30	6:30
7:00		7:00	7:00
7:30		7:30	7:30
8:00		8:00	8:00
8:30		8:30	8:30
9:00		9:00	9:00
9:30		9:30	9:30
10:00		10:00	10:00
10:30		10:30	10:30
11:00		11:00	11:00

Ready for tomorrow?	( )	( )	( )
ALARM			
CLOTHES/BACKPACK			
GLASS OF WATER			
SAVERS PREP			
BEDTIME AFFIRMATIONS			

Wednesday		Thursday		Friday		Saturday	
S		S		S		S	
A		A		A		A	
V		V		V		V	
E		E		E		E	
R		R		R		R	
S		S		S		S	
◆		◆		◆		◆	
◆		◆		◆		◆	
5:00		5:00		5:00		5:00	
5:30		5:30		5:30		5:30	
6:00		6:00		6:00		6:00	
6:30		6:30		6:30		6:30	
7:00		7:00		7:00		7:00	
7:30		7:30		7:30		7:30	
8:00		8:00		8:00		8:00	
8:30		8:30		8:30		8:30	
9:00		9:00		9:00		9:00	
9:30		9:30		9:30		9:30	
10:00		10:00		10:00		10:00	
10:30		10:30		10:30		10:30	
11:00		11:00		11:00		11:00	
11:30		11:30		11:30		11:30	
12:00		12:00		12:00		12:00	
12:30		12:30		12:30		12:30	
1:00		1:00		1:00		1:00	
1:30		1:30		1:30		1:30	
2:00		2:00		2:00		2:00	
2:30		2:30		2:30		2:30	
3:00		3:00		3:00		3:00	
3:30		3:30		3:30		3:30	
4:00		4:00		4:00		4:00	
4:30		4:30		4:30		4:30	
5:00		5:00		5:00		5:00	
5:30		5:30		5:30		5:30	
6:00		6:00		6:00		6:00	
6:30		6:30		6:30		6:30	
7:00		7:00		7:00		7:00	
7:30		7:30		7:30		7:30	
8:00		8:00		8:00		8:00	
8:30		8:30		8:30		8:30	
9:00		9:00		9:00		9:00	
9:30		9:30		9:30		9:30	
10:00		10:00		10:00		10:00	
10:30		10:30		10:30		10:30	
11:00		11:00		11:00		11:00	
	( )		( )		( )		( )

WEEKLY REFLECTION

....

1) What was my greatest accomplishment this week?

2) Who or what am I grateful for?

3) What activity from this last week took away from my focus and time?

4) What is one thing I can do to be better prepared for this week?

5) What am I looking forward to during the upcoming week?

BRAINSTORM

FINANCIAL CHECKBOX

Questions	Yes	No
Did I remain on budget this week?		
Did I buy what I needed over what I wanted?		
If you got paid this week, did you place 10% of it in your savings?		
Have I taken a percentage (1%-10%) to donate?		
Did I use my credit card wisely this week?		
How can I manage my money more wisely this week?		

Week of:	Sunday	Monday	Tuesday
This Week's Goal	S	S	S
	A	A	A
	V	V	V
	E	E	E
	R	R	R
	S	S	S
Intention for the Day	◆	◆	◆
Grateful for ...	◆	◆	◆

	Sunday	Monday	Tuesday
We make a living by what we get. We make a life by what we give. —WINSTON CHURCHILL	5:00	5:00	5:00
	5:30	5:30	5:30
	6:00	6:00	6:00
	6:30	6:30	6:30
	7:00	7:00	7:00
	7:30	7:30	7:30
	8:00	8:00	8:00
	8:30	8:30	8:30
	9:00	9:00	9:00
	9:30	9:30	9:30
TO-DO LIST	10:00	10:00	10:00
Highest Priority	10:30	10:30	10:30
	11:00	11:00	11:00
	11:30	11:30	11:30
	12:00	12:00	12:00
	12:30	12:30	12:30
	1:00	1:00	1:00
Definite Priority	1:30	1:30	1:30
	2:00	2:00	2:00
	2:30	2:30	2:30
	3:00	3:00	3:00
	3:30	3:30	3:30
	4:00	4:00	4:00
Lowest Priority	4:30	4:30	4:30
	5:00	5:00	5:00
	5:30	5:30	5:30
	6:00	6:00	6:00
	6:30	6:30	6:30
	7:00	7:00	7:00
	7:30	7:30	7:30
Habit to Work on This Week	8:00	8:00	8:00
	8:30	8:30	8:30
	9:00	9:00	9:00
	9:30	9:30	9:30
	10:00	10:00	10:00
	10:30	10:30	10:30
	11:00	11:00	11:00

Ready for tomorrow?	( )	( )	( )
ALARM			
CLOTHES/BACKPACK			
GLASS OF WATER			
SAVERS PREP			
BEDTIME AFFIRMATIONS			

Wednesday	Thursday	Friday	Saturday
S	S	S	S
A	A	A	A
V	V	V	V
E	E	E	E
R	R	R	R
S	S	S	S
◆	◆	◆	◆
◆	◆	◆	◆

Wednesday	Thursday	Friday	Saturday
5:00	5:00	5:00	5:00
5:30	5:30	5:30	5:30
6:00	6:00	6:00	6:00
6:30	6:30	6:30	6:30
7:00	7:00	7:00	7:00
7:30	7:30	7:30	7:30
8:00	8:00	8:00	8:00
8:30	8:30	8:30	8:30
9:00	9:00	9:00	9:00
9:30	9:30	9:30	9:30
10:00	10:00	10:00	10:00
10:30	10:30	10:30	10:30
11:00	11:00	11:00	11:00
11:30	11:30	11:30	11:30
12:00	12:00	12:00	12:00
12:30	12:30	12:30	12:30
1:00	1:00	1:00	1:00
1:30	1:30	1:30	1:30
2:00	2:00	2:00	2:00
2:30	2:30	2:30	2:30
3:00	3:00	3:00	3:00
3:30	3:30	3:30	3:30
4:00	4:00	4:00	4:00
4:30	4:30	4:30	4:30
5:00	5:00	5:00	5:00
5:30	5:30	5:30	5:30
6:00	6:00	6:00	6:00
6:30	6:30	6:30	6:30
7:00	7:00	7:00	7:00
7:30	7:30	7:30	7:30
8:00	8:00	8:00	8:00
8:30	8:30	8:30	8:30
9:00	9:00	9:00	9:00
9:30	9:30	9:30	9:30
10:00	10:00	10:00	10:00
10:30	10:30	10:30	10:30
11:00	11:00	11:00	11:00

( )	( )	( )	( )

WEEKLY REFLECTION

. . . .

1) What was my greatest accomplishment this week?

2) Who or what am I grateful for?

3) What activity from this last week took away from my focus and time?

4) What is one thing I can do to be better prepared for this week?

5) What am I looking forward to during the upcoming week?

BRAINSTORM

FINANCIAL CHECKBOX

Questions	Yes	No
Did I remain on budget this week?		
Did I buy what I needed over what I wanted?		
If you got paid this week, did you place 10% of it in your savings?		
Have I taken a percentage (1%-10%) to donate?		
Did I use my credit card wisely this week?		

How can I manage my money more wisely this week?

Week of:	Sunday	Monday	Tuesday
This Week's Goal	S	S	S
	A	A	A
	V	V	V
	E	E	E
	R	R	R
	S	S	S

Intention for the Day	◆	◆	◆
Grateful for ...	◆	◆	◆

You've got to get up every morning with determination if you're going to go to bed with satisfaction.

—GEORGE LORIMER

TO-DO LIST

Highest Priority

Definite Priority

Lowest Priority

Habit to Work on This Week

Time	Sunday	Monday	Tuesday
5:00			
5:30			
6:00			
6:30			
7:00			
7:30			
8:00			
8:30			
9:00			
9:30			
10:00			
10:30			
11:00			
11:30			
12:00			
12:30			
1:00			
1:30			
2:00			
2:30			
3:00			
3:30			
4:00			
4:30			
5:00			
5:30			
6:00			
6:30			
7:00			
7:30			
8:00			
8:30			
9:00			
9:30			
10:00			
10:30			
11:00			

Ready for tomorrow?	( )	( )	( )
ALARM			
CLOTHES/BACKPACK			
GLASS OF WATER			
SAVERS PREP			
BEDTIME AFFIRMATIONS			

Wednesday		Thursday		Friday		Saturday	
S		S		S		S	
A		A		A		A	
V		V		V		V	
E		E		E		E	
R		R		R		R	
S		S		S		S	
◆		◆		◆		◆	
◆		◆		◆		◆	
5:00		5:00		5:00		5:00	
5:30		5:30		5:30		5:30	
6:00		6:00		6:00		6:00	
6:30		6:30		6:30		6:30	
7:00		7:00		7:00		7:00	
7:30		7:30		7:30		7:30	
8:00		8:00		8:00		8:00	
8:30		8:30		8:30		8:30	
9:00		9:00		9:00		9:00	
9:30		9:30		9:30		9:30	
10:00		10:00		10:00		10:00	
10:30		10:30		10:30		10:30	
11:00		11:00		11:00		11:00	
11:30		11:30		11:30		11:30	
12:00		12:00		12:00		12:00	
12:30		12:30		12:30		12:30	
1:00		1:00		1:00		1:00	
1:30		1:30		1:30		1:30	
2:00		2:00		2:00		2:00	
2:30		2:30		2:30		2:30	
3:00		3:00		3:00		3:00	
3:30		3:30		3:30		3:30	
4:00		4:00		4:00		4:00	
4:30		4:30		4:30		4:30	
5:00		5:00		5:00		5:00	
5:30		5:30		5:30		5:30	
6:00		6:00		6:00		6:00	
6:30		6:30		6:30		6:30	
7:00		7:00		7:00		7:00	
7:30		7:30		7:30		7:30	
8:00		8:00		8:00		8:00	
8:30		8:30		8:30		8:30	
9:00		9:00		9:00		9:00	
9:30		9:30		9:30		9:30	
10:00		10:00		10:00		10:00	
10:30		10:30		10:30		10:30	
11:00		11:00		11:00		11:00	
	( )		( )		( )		( )

WEEKLY REFLECTION

• •

1) What was my greatest accomplishment this week?

2) Who or what am I grateful for?

3) What activity from this last week took away from my focus and time?

4) What is one thing I can do to be better prepared for this week?

5) What am I looking forward to during the upcoming week?

BRAINSTORM

FINANCIAL CHECKBOX

Questions	Yes	No
Did I remain on budget this week?		
Did I buy what I needed over what I wanted?		
If you got paid this week, did you place 10% of it in your savings?		
Have I taken a percentage (1%-10%) to donate?		
Did I use my credit card wisely this week?		

How can I manage my money more wisely this week?

Week of:		Sunday		Monday		Tuesday
This Week's Goal		S		S		S
		A		A		A
		V		V		V
		E		E		E
		R		R		R
		S		S		S

Intention for the Day	◆	◆	◆
Grateful for ...	◆	◆	◆

Your level of success will seldom exceed your level of personal development ... because success is something you attract by the person you become.

—JIM ROHN

TO-DO LIST
Highest Priority
Definite Priority
Lowest Priority
Habit to Work on This Week

Time	Sunday	Monday	Tuesday
5:00			
5:30			
6:00			
6:30			
7:00			
7:30			
8:00			
8:30			
9:00			
9:30			
10:00			
10:30			
11:00			
11:30			
12:00			
12:30			
1:00			
1:30			
2:00			
2:30			
3:00			
3:30			
4:00			
4:30			
5:00			
5:30			
6:00			
6:30			
7:00			
7:30			
8:00			
8:30			
9:00			
9:30			
10:00			
10:30			
11:00			

Ready for tomorrow?		( )		( )		( )
ALARM						
CLOTHES/BACKPACK						
GLASS OF WATER						
SAVERS PREP						
BEDTIME AFFIRMATIONS						

Wednesday	Thursday	Friday	Saturday
S	S	S	S
A	A	A	A
V	V	V	V
E	E	E	E
R	R	R	R
S	S	S	S

◆		◆		◆		◆	
		◆		◆		◆	
◆		◆		◆		◆	

Wednesday	Thursday	Friday	Saturday
5:00	5:00	5:00	5:00
5:30	5:30	5:30	5:30
6:00	6:00	6:00	6:00
6:30	6:30	6:30	6:30
7:00	7:00	7:00	7:00
7:30	7:30	7:30	7:30
8:00	8:00	8:00	8:00
8:30	8:30	8:30	8:30
9:00	9:00	9:00	9:00
9:30	9:30	9:30	9:30
10:00	10:00	10:00	10:00
10:30	10:30	10:30	10:30
11:00	11:00	11:00	11:00
11:30	11:30	11:30	11:30
12:00	12:00	12:00	12:00
12:30	12:30	12:30	12:30
1:00	1:00	1:00	1:00
1:30	1:30	1:30	1:30
2:00	2:00	2:00	2:00
2:30	2:30	2:30	2:30
3:00	3:00	3:00	3:00
3:30	3:30	3:30	3:30
4:00	4:00	4:00	4:00
4:30	4:30	4:30	4:30
5:00	5:00	5:00	5:00
5:30	5:30	5:30	5:30
6:00	6:00	6:00	6:00
6:30	6:30	6:30	6:30
7:00	7:00	7:00	7:00
7:30	7:30	7:30	7:30
8:00	8:00	8:00	8:00
8:30	8:30	8:30	8:30
9:00	9:00	9:00	9:00
9:30	9:30	9:30	9:30
10:00	10:00	10:00	10:00
10:30	10:30	10:30	10:30
11:00	11:00	11:00	11:00

( )	( )	( )	( )

WEEKLY REFLECTION

....

1) What was my greatest accomplishment this week?

2) Who or what am I grateful for?

3) What activity from this last week took away from my focus and time?

4) What is one thing I can do to be better prepared for this week?

5) What am I looking forward to during the upcoming week?

BRAINSTORM

FINANCIAL CHECKBOX

Questions	Yes	No
Did I remain on budget this week?		
Did I buy what I needed over what I wanted?		
If you got paid this week, did you place 10% of it in your savings?		
Have I taken a percentage (1%-10%) to donate?		
Did I use my credit card wisely this week?		
How can I manage my money more wisely this week?		

Week of:	Sunday		Monday		Tuesday	
This Week's Goal	S		S		S	
	A		A		A	
	V		V		V	
	E		E		E	
	R		R		R	
	S		S		S	
Intention for the Day	◆		◆		◆	
Grateful for ...	◆		◆		◆	

Make each day your masterpiece.

—JOHN WOODEN

TO-DO LIST		Sunday		Monday		Tuesday
Highest Priority	5:00		5:00		5:00	
	5:30		5:30		5:30	
	6:00		6:00		6:00	
	6:30		6:30		6:30	
	7:00		7:00		7:00	
	7:30		7:30		7:30	
	8:00		8:00		8:00	
	8:30		8:30		8:30	
	9:00		9:00		9:00	
	9:30		9:30		9:30	
	10:00		10:00		10:00	
	10:30		10:30		10:30	
	11:00		11:00		11:00	
	11:30		11:30		11:30	
	12:00		12:00		12:00	
	12:30		12:30		12:30	
	1:00		1:00		1:00	
Definite Priority	1:30		1:30		1:30	
	2:00		2:00		2:00	
	2:30		2:30		2:30	
	3:00		3:00		3:00	
	3:30		3:30		3:30	
	4:00		4:00		4:00	
Lowest Priority	4:30		4:30		4:30	
	5:00		5:00		5:00	
	5:30		5:30		5:30	
	6:00		6:00		6:00	
	6:30		6:30		6:30	
	7:00		7:00		7:00	
	7:30		7:30		7:30	
Habit to Work on This Week	8:00		8:00		8:00	
	8:30		8:30		8:30	
	9:00		9:00		9:00	
	9:30		9:30		9:30	
	10:00		10:00		10:00	
	10:30		10:30		10:30	
	11:00		11:00		11:00	

Ready for tomorrow?	( )	( )	( )
ALARM			
CLOTHES/BACKPACK			
GLASS OF WATER			
SAVERS PREP			
BEDTIME AFFIRMATIONS			

Wednesday	Thursday	Friday	Saturday
S	S	S	S
A	A	A	A
V	V	V	V
E	E	E	E
R	R	R	R
S	S	S	S

◆	◆	◆	◆
◆	◆	◆	◆

Wednesday		Thursday		Friday		Saturday	
5:00		5:00		5:00		5:00	
5:30		5:30		5:30		5:30	
6:00		6:00		6:00		6:00	
6:30		6:30		6:30		6:30	
7:00		7:00		7:00		7:00	
7:30		7:30		7:30		7:30	
8:00		8:00		8:00		8:00	
8:30		8:30		8:30		8:30	
9:00		9:00		9:00		9:00	
9:30		9:30		9:30		9:30	
10:00		10:00		10:00		10:00	
10:30		10:30		10:30		10:30	
11:00		11:00		11:00		11:00	
11:30		11:30		11:30		11:30	
12:00		12:00		12:00		12:00	
12:30		12:30		12:30		12:30	
1:00		1:00		1:00		1:00	
1:30		1:30		1:30		1:30	
2:00		2:00		2:00		2:00	
2:30		2:30		2:30		2:30	
3:00		3:00		3:00		3:00	
3:30		3:30		3:30		3:30	
4:00		4:00		4:00		4:00	
4:30		4:30		4:30		4:30	
5:00		5:00		5:00		5:00	
5:30		5:30		5:30		5:30	
6:00		6:00		6:00		6:00	
6:30		6:30		6:30		6:30	
7:00		7:00		7:00		7:00	
7:30		7:30		7:30		7:30	
8:00		8:00		8:00		8:00	
8:30		8:30		8:30		8:30	
9:00		9:00		9:00		9:00	
9:30		9:30		9:30		9:30	
10:00		10:00		10:00		10:00	
10:30		10:30		10:30		10:30	
11:00		11:00		11:00		11:00	

( )	( )	( )	( )

WEEKLY REFLECTION

• •

1) What was my greatest accomplishment this week?

2) Who or what am I grateful for?

3) What activity from this last week took away from my focus and time?

4) What is one thing I can do to be better prepared for this week?

5) What am I looking forward to during the upcoming week?

BRAINSTORM

FINANCIAL CHECKBOX

Questions	Yes	No
Did I remain on budget this week?		
Did I buy what I needed over what I wanted?		
If you got paid this week, did you place 10% of it in your savings?		
Have I taken a percentage (1%-10%) to donate?		
Did I use my credit card wisely this week?		

How can I manage my money more wisely this week?

MONTHLY REFLECTION

● ●

Write 5 things you accomplished this month:

1.

2.

3.

4.

5.

QUESTIONS

1) What did I learn about myself this month?

2) What tasks are left over from this month that are lingering and need to get done?

3. Did I take care of myself?

4) What could I have done differently this past month?

5) What areas can I (still) improve on?

6) What experiences can I treasure?

7) What challenged me and how did I overcome the challenge?

8) What specific habits and/or rituals could I develop this month to support my vision?

MONTH OF:	SUNDAY	MONDAY	TUESDAY
This Month's Goal			
Important Events or Reminders to Transfer to My Phone			
1.			
2.			
3.			
4.			
5.			
6.			
7.			
8.			
9.			
10.			

PROJECT NAME	CLASS & INSTRUCTOR	IMPORTANT DATES	DEADLINES
1.			
2.			
3.			
4.			

WEDNESDAY	THURSDAY	FRIDAY	SATURDAY

BRAINSTORM

Week of:	Sunday	Monday	Tuesday
This Week's Goal	S	S	S
	A	A	A
	V	V	V
	E	E	E
	R	R	R
	S	S	S
Intention for the Day	◆	◆	◆
Grateful for ...	◆	◆	◆

	Sunday	Monday	Tuesday
Remember, the moment you accept total responsibility for everything in your life is the moment you claim the power to change anything in your life. —**HAL ELROD**	5:00	5:00	5:00
	5:30	5:30	5:30
	6:00	6:00	6:00
	6:30	6:30	6:30
	7:00	7:00	7:00
	7:30	7:30	7:30
	8:00	8:00	8:00
	8:30	8:30	8:30
	9:00	9:00	9:00
	9:30	9:30	9:30
TO-DO LIST	10:00	10:00	10:00
Highest Priority	10:30	10:30	10:30
	11:00	11:00	11:00
	11:30	11:30	11:30
	12:00	12:00	12:00
	12:30	12:30	12:30
	1:00	1:00	1:00
Definite Priority	1:30	1:30	1:30
	2:00	2:00	2:00
	2:30	2:30	2:30
	3:00	3:00	3:00
	3:30	3:30	3:30
	4:00	4:00	4:00
Lowest Priority	4:30	4:30	4:30
	5:00	5:00	5:00
	5:30	5:30	5:30
	6:00	6:00	6:00
	6:30	6:30	6:30
	7:00	7:00	7:00
	7:30	7:30	7:30
Habit to Work on This Week	8:00	8:00	8:00
	8:30	8:30	8:30
	9:00	9:00	9:00
	9:30	9:30	9:30
	10:00	10:00	10:00
	10:30	10:30	10:30
	11:00	11:00	11:00

Ready for tomorrow?	( )	( )	( )
ALARM			
CLOTHES/BACKPACK			
GLASS OF WATER			
SAVERS PREP			
BEDTIME AFFIRMATIONS			

Wednesday		Thursday		Friday		Saturday	
S		S		S		S	
A		A		A		A	
V		V		V		V	
E		E		E		E	
R		R		R		R	
S		S		S		S	
◆		◆		◆		◆	
◆		◆		◆		◆	

Wednesday	Thursday	Friday	Saturday
5:00	5:00	5:00	5:00
5:30	5:30	5:30	5:30
6:00	6:00	6:00	6:00
6:30	6:30	6:30	6:30
7:00	7:00	7:00	7:00
7:30	7:30	7:30	7:30
8:00	8:00	8:00	8:00
8:30	8:30	8:30	8:30
9:00	9:00	9:00	9:00
9:30	9:30	9:30	9:30
10:00	10:00	10:00	10:00
10:30	10:30	10:30	10:30
11:00	11:00	11:00	11:00
11:30	11:30	11:30	11:30
12:00	12:00	12:00	12:00
12:30	12:30	12:30	12:30
1:00	1:00	1:00	1:00
1:30	1:30	1:30	1:30
2:00	2:00	2:00	2:00
2:30	2:30	2:30	2:30
3:00	3:00	3:00	3:00
3:30	3:30	3:30	3:30
4:00	4:00	4:00	4:00
4:30	4:30	4:30	4:30
5:00	5:00	5:00	5:00
5:30	5:30	5:30	5:30
6:00	6:00	6:00	6:00
6:30	6:30	6:30	6:30
7:00	7:00	7:00	7:00
7:30	7:30	7:30	7:30
8:00	8:00	8:00	8:00
8:30	8:30	8:30	8:30
9:00	9:00	9:00	9:00
9:30	9:30	9:30	9:30
10:00	10:00	10:00	10:00
10:30	10:30	10:30	10:30
11:00	11:00	11:00	

( )	( )	( )	( )

WEEKLY REFLECTION

• •

1) What was my greatest accomplishment this week?

2) Who or what am I grateful for?

3) What activity from this last week took away from my focus and time?

4) What is one thing I can do to be better prepared for this week?

5) What am I looking forward to during the upcoming week?

BRAINSTORM

FINANCIAL CHECKBOX

Questions	Yes	No
Did I remain on budget this week?		
Did I buy what I needed over what I wanted?		
If you got paid this week, did you place 10% of it in your savings?		
Have I taken a percentage (1%-10%) to donate?		
Did I use my credit card wisely this week?		

How can I manage my money more wisely this week?

Week of:		Sunday		Monday		Tuesday
This Week's Goal		S		S		S
		A		A		A
		V		V		V
		E		E		E
		R		R		R
		S		S		S
Intention for the Day		◆		◆		◆
Grateful for ...		◆		◆		◆

	Sunday	Monday	Tuesday
To make profound changes in your life, you need either inspiration or desperation. —ANTHONY ROBBINS	5:00	5:00	5:00
	5:30	5:30	5:30
	6:00	6:00	6:00
	6:30	6:30	6:30
	7:00	7:00	7:00
	7:30	7:30	7:30
	8:00	8:00	8:00
	8:30	8:30	8:30
	9:00	9:00	9:00
	9:30	9:30	9:30
TO-DO LIST	10:00	10:00	10:00
Highest Priority	10:30	10:30	10:30
	11:00	11:00	11:00
	11:30	11:30	11:30
	12:00	12:00	12:00
	12:30	12:30	12:30
	1:00	1:00	1:00
Definite Priority	1:30	1:30	1:30
	2:00	2:00	2:00
	2:30	2:30	2:30
	3:00	3:00	3:00
	3:30	3:30	3:30
	4:00	4:00	4:00
Lowest Priority	4:30	4:30	4:30
	5:00	5:00	5:00
	5:30	5:30	5:30
	6:00	6:00	6:00
	6:30	6:30	6:30
	7:00	7:00	7:00
	7:30	7:30	7:30
Habit to Work on This Week	8:00	8:00	8:00
	8:30	8:30	8:30
	9:00	9:00	9:00
	9:30	9:30	9:30
	10:00	10:00	10:00
	10:30	10:30	10:30
	11:00	11:00	11:00

Ready for tomorrow?		( )		( )		( )
ALARM						
CLOTHES/BACKPACK						
GLASS OF WATER						
SAVERS PREP						
BEDTIME AFFIRMATIONS						

Wednesday		Thursday		Friday		Saturday	
S		S		S		S	
A		A		A		A	
V		V		V		V	
E		E		E		E	
R		R		R		R	
S		S		S		S	

◆		◆		◆		◆	
◆		◆		◆		◆	

Wednesday		Thursday		Friday		Saturday	
5:00		5:00		5:00		5:00	
5:30		5:30		5:30		5:30	
6:00		6:00		6:00		6:00	
6:30		6:30		6:30		6:30	
7:00		7:00		7:00		7:00	
7:30		7:30		7:30		7:30	
8:00		8:00		8:00		8:00	
8:30		8:30		8:30		8:30	
9:00		9:00		9:00		9:00	
9:30		9:30		9:30		9:30	
10:00		10:00		10:00		10:00	
10:30		10:30		10:30		10:30	
11:00		11:00		11:00		11:00	
11:30		11:30		11:30		11:30	
12:00		12:00		12:00		12:00	
12:30		12:30		12:30		12:30	
1:00		1:00		1:00		1:00	
1:30		1:30		1:30		1:30	
2:00		2:00		2:00		2:00	
2:30		2:30		2:30		2:30	
3:00		3:00		3:00		3:00	
3:30		3:30		3:30		3:30	
4:00		4:00		4:00		4:00	
4:30		4:30		4:30		4:30	
5:00		5:00		5:00		5:00	
5:30		5:30		5:30		5:30	
6:00		6:00		6:00		6:00	
6:30		6:30		6:30		6:30	
7:00		7:00		7:00		7:00	
7:30		7:30		7:30		7:30	
8:00		8:00		8:00		8:00	
8:30		8:30		8:30		8:30	
9:00		9:00		9:00		9:00	
9:30		9:30		9:30		9:30	
10:00		10:00		10:00		10:00	
10:30		10:30		10:30		10:30	
11:00		11:00		11:00		11:00	
	( )		( )		( )		( )

WEEKLY REFLECTION

• •

1) What was my greatest accomplishment this week?

2) Who or what am I grateful for?

3) What activity from this last week took away from my focus and time?

4) What is one thing I can do to be better prepared for this week?

5) What am I looking forward to during the upcoming week?

BRAINSTORM

FINANCIAL CHECKBOX

Questions	Yes	No
Did I remain on budget this week?		
Did I buy what I needed over what I wanted?		
If you got paid this week, did you place 10% of it in your savings?		
Have I taken a percentage (1%-10%) to donate?		
Did I use my credit card wisely this week?		

How can I manage my money more wisely this week?

Week of:	Sunday	Monday	Tuesday
This Week's Goal	S	S	S
	A	A	A
	V	V	V
	E	E	E
	R	R	R
	S	S	S
Intention for the Day	◆	◆	◆
Grateful for ...	◆	◆	◆

	Sunday	Monday	Tuesday
	5:00	5:00	5:00
	5:30	5:30	5:30
Don't chase money.	6:00	6:00	6:00
Chase excellence.	6:30	6:30	6:30
	7:00	7:00	7:00
—JEFF HOFFMAN	7:30	7:30	7:30
	8:00	8:00	8:00
	8:30	8:30	8:30
	9:00	9:00	9:00
	9:30	9:30	9:30
TO-DO LIST	10:00	10:00	10:00
Highest Priority	10:30	10:30	10:30
	11:00	11:00	11:00
	11:30	11:30	11:30
	12:00	12:00	12:00
	12:30	12:30	12:30
	1:00	1:00	1:00
Definite Priority	1:30	1:30	1:30
	2:00	2:00	2:00
	2:30	2:30	2:30
	3:00	3:00	3:00
	3:30	3:30	3:30
	4:00	4:00	4:00
Lowest Priority	4:30	4:30	4:30
	5:00	5:00	5:00
	5:30	5:30	5:30
	6:00	6:00	6:00
	6:30	6:30	6:30
	7:00	7:00	7:00
	7:30	7:30	7:30
Habit to Work on This Week	8:00	8:00	8:00
	8:30	8:30	8:30
	9:00	9:00	9:00
	9:30	9:30	9:30
	10:00	10:00	10:00
	10:30	10:30	10:30
	11:00	11:00	11:00

Ready for tomorrow?	( )	( )	( )
ALARM			
CLOTHES/BACKPACK			
GLASS OF WATER			
SAVERS PREP			
BEDTIME AFFIRMATIONS			

Wednesday	Thursday	Friday	Saturday
S	S	S	S
A	A	A	A
V	V	V	V
E	E	E	E
R	R	R	R
S	S	S	S
◆	◆	◆	◆
◆	◆	◆	◆

	Wednesday		Thursday		Friday		Saturday
5:00		5:00		5:00		5:00	
5:30		5:30		5:30		5:30	
6:00		6:00		6:00		6:00	
6:30		6:30		6:30		6:30	
7:00		7:00		7:00		7:00	
7:30		7:30		7:30		7:30	
8:00		8:00		8:00		8:00	
8:30		8:30		8:30		8:30	
9:00		9:00		9:00		9:00	
9:30		9:30		9:30		9:30	
10:00		10:00		10:00		10:00	
10:30		10:30		10:30		10:30	
11:00		11:00		11:00		11:00	
11:30		11:30		11:30		11:30	
12:00		12:00		12:00		12:00	
12:30		12:30		12:30		12:30	
1:00		1:00		1:00		1:00	
1:30		1:30		1:30		1:30	
2:00		2:00		2:00		2:00	
2:30		2:30		2:30		2:30	
3:00		3:00		3:00		3:00	
3:30		3:30		3:30		3:30	
4:00		4:00		4:00		4:00	
4:30		4:30		4:30		4:30	
5:00		5:00		5:00		5:00	
5:30		5:30		5:30		5:30	
6:00		6:00		6:00		6:00	
6:30		6:30		6:30		6:30	
7:00		7:00		7:00		7:00	
7:30		7:30		7:30		7:30	
8:00		8:00		8:00		8:00	
8:30		8:30		8:30		8:30	
9:00		9:00		9:00		9:00	
9:30		9:30		9:30		9:30	
10:00		10:00		10:00		10:00	
10:30		10:30		10:30		10:30	
11:00		11:00		11:00		11:00	
	( )		( )		( )		( )

WEEKLY REFLECTION

• •

1) What was my greatest accomplishment this week?

2) Who or what am I grateful for?

3) What activity from this last week took away from my focus and time?

4) What is one thing I can do to be better prepared for this week?

5) What am I looking forward to during the upcoming week?

BRAINSTORM

FINANCIAL CHECKBOX

Questions	Yes	No
Did I remain on budget this week?		
Did I buy what I needed over what I wanted?		
If you got paid this week, did you place 10% of it in your savings?		
Have I taken a percentage (1%-10%) to donate?		
Did I use my credit card wisely this week?		

How can I manage my money more wisely this week?

Week of:	Sunday	Monday	Tuesday
This Week's Goal	S	S	S
	A	A	A
	V	V	V
	E	E	E
	R	R	R
	S	S	S
Intention for the Day	◆	◆	◆
Grateful for ...	◆	◆	◆

	Sunday	Monday	Tuesday
If you look at what you have in life, you'll always have more. If you look at what you don't have in life, you'll never have enough. **—OPRAH WINFREY**	5:00	5:00	5:00
	5:30	5:30	5:30
	6:00	6:00	6:00
	6:30	6:30	6:30
	7:00	7:00	7:00
	7:30	7:30	7:30
	8:00	8:00	8:00
	8:30	8:30	8:30
	9:00	9:00	9:00
	9:30	9:30	9:30
TO-DO LIST	10:00	10:00	10:00
Highest Priority	10:30	10:30	10:30
	11:00	11:00	11:00
	11:30	11:30	11:30
	12:00	12:00	12:00
	12:30	12:30	12:30
	1:00	1:00	1:00
Definite Priority	1:30	1:30	1:30
	2:00	2:00	2:00
	2:30	2:30	2:30
	3:00	3:00	3:00
	3:30	3:30	3:30
	4:00	4:00	4:00
Lowest Priority	4:30	4:30	4:30
	5:00	5:00	5:00
	5:30	5:30	5:30
	6:00	6:00	6:00
	6:30	6:30	6:30
	7:00	7:00	7:00
	7:30	7:30	7:30
Habit to Work on This Week	8:00	8:00	8:00
	8:30	8:30	8:30
	9:00	9:00	9:00
	9:30	9:30	9:30
	10:00	10:00	10:00
	10:30	10:30	10:30
	11:00	11:00	11:00

Ready for tomorrow?	( )	( )	( )
ALARM			
CLOTHES/BACKPACK			
GLASS OF WATER			
SAVERS PREP			
BEDTIME AFFIRMATIONS			

Wednesday		Thursday		Friday		Saturday	
S		S		S		S	
A		A		A		A	
V		V		V		V	
E		E		E		E	
R		R		R		R	
S		S		S		S	
◆		◆		◆		◆	
◆		◆		◆		◆	
5:00		5:00		5:00		5:00	
5:30		5:30		5:30		5:30	
6:00		6:00		6:00		6:00	
6:30		6:30		6:30		6:30	
7:00		7:00		7:00		7:00	
7:30		7:30		7:30		7:30	
8:00		8:00		8:00		8:00	
8:30		8:30		8:30		8:30	
9:00		9:00		9:00		9:00	
9:30		9:30		9:30		9:30	
10:00		10:00		10:00		10:00	
10:30		10:30		10:30		10:30	
11:00		11:00		11:00		11:00	
11:30		11:30		11:30		11:30	
12:00		12:00		12:00		12:00	
12:30		12:30		12:30		12:30	
1:00		1:00		1:00		1:00	
1:30		1:30		1:30		1:30	
2:00		2:00		2:00		2:00	
2:30		2:30		2:30		2:30	
3:00		3:00		3:00		3:00	
3:30		3:30		3:30		3:30	
4:00		4:00		4:00		4:00	
4:30		4:30		4:30		4:30	
5:00		5:00		5:00		5:00	
5:30		5:30		5:30		5:30	
6:00		6:00		6:00		6:00	
6:30		6:30		6:30		6:30	
7:00		7:00		7:00		7:00	
7:30		7:30		7:30		7:30	
8:00		8:00		8:00		8:00	
8:30		8:30		8:30		8:30	
9:00		9:00		9:00		9:00	
9:30		9:30		9:30		9:30	
10:00		10:00		10:00		10:00	
10:30		10:30		10:30		10:30	
11:00		11:00		11:00		11:00	
	( )		( )		( )		( )

WEEKLY REFLECTION

....

1) What was my greatest accomplishment this week?

2) Who or what am I grateful for?

3) What activity from this last week took away from my focus and time?

4) What is one thing I can do to be better prepared for this week?

5) What am I looking forward to during the upcoming week?

BRAINSTORM

FINANCIAL CHECKBOX

Questions	Yes	No
Did I remain on budget this week?		
Did I buy what I needed over what I wanted?		
If you got paid this week, did you place 10% of it in your savings?		
Have I taken a percentage (1%-10%) to donate?		
Did I use my credit card wisely this week?		

How can I manage my money more wisely this week?

Week of:	Sunday		Monday		Tuesday	
This Week's Goal	S		S		S	
	A		A		A	
	V		V		V	
	E		E		E	
	R		R		R	
	S		S		S	
Intention for the Day	◆		◆		◆	
Grateful for ...	◆		◆		◆	

Set an incredible goal- not to achieve the goal itself- but to become who you must become to achieve it.

—HONORÉE CORDER

TO-DO LIST
Highest Priority
Definite Priority
Lowest Priority
Habit to Work on This Week

Sunday	Monday	Tuesday
5:00	5:00	5:00
5:30	5:30	5:30
6:00	6:00	6:00
6:30	6:30	6:30
7:00	7:00	7:00
7:30	7:30	7:30
8:00	8:00	8:00
8:30	8:30	8:30
9:00	9:00	9:00
9:30	9:30	9:30
10:00	10:00	10:00
10:30	10:30	10:30
11:00	11:00	11:00
11:30	11:30	11:30
12:00	12:00	12:00
12:30	12:30	12:30
1:00	1:00	1:00
1:30	1:30	1:30
2:00	2:00	2:00
2:30	2:30	2:30
3:00	3:00	3:00
3:30	3:30	3:30
4:00	4:00	4:00
4:30	4:30	4:30
5:00	5:00	5:00
5:30	5:30	5:30
6:00	6:00	6:00
6:30	6:30	6:30
7:00	7:00	7:00
7:30	7:30	7:30
8:00	8:00	8:00
8:30	8:30	8:30
9:00	9:00	9:00
9:30	9:30	9:30
10:00	10:00	10:00
10:30	10:30	10:30
11:00	11:00	11:00

Ready for tomorrow?	( )	( )	( )
ALARM			
CLOTHES/BACKPACK			
GLASS OF WATER			
SAVERS PREP			
BEDTIME AFFIRMATIONS			

Wednesday	Thursday	Friday	Saturday
S	S	S	S
A	A	A	A
V	V	V	V
E	E	E	E
R	R	R	R
S	S	S	S

◆	◆	◆	◆
◆	◆	◆	◆

Wednesday	Thursday	Friday	Saturday
5:00	5:00	5:00	5:00
5:30	5:30	5:30	5:30
6:00	6:00	6:00	6:00
6:30	6:30	6:30	6:30
7:00	7:00	7:00	7:00
7:30	7:30	7:30	7:30
8:00	8:00	8:00	8:00
8:30	8:30	8:30	8:30
9:00	9:00	9:00	9:00
9:30	9:30	9:30	9:30
10:00	10:00	10:00	10:00
10:30	10:30	10:30	10:30
11:00	11:00	11:00	11:00
11:30	11:30	11:30	11:30
12:00	12:00	12:00	12:00
12:30	12:30	12:30	12:30
1:00	1:00	1:00	1:00
1:30	1:30	1:30	1:30
2:00	2:00	2:00	2:00
2:30	2:30	2:30	2:30
3:00	3:00	3:00	3:00
3:30	3:30	3:30	3:30
4:00	4:00	4:00	4:00
4:30	4:30	4:30	4:30
5:00	5:00	5:00	5:00
5:30	5:30	5:30	5:30
6:00	6:00	6:00	6:00
6:30	6:30	6:30	6:30
7:00	7:00	7:00	7:00
7:30	7:30	7:30	7:30
8:00	8:00	8:00	8:00
8:30	8:30	8:30	8:30
9:00	9:00	9:00	9:00
9:30	9:30	9:30	9:30
10:00	10:00	10:00	10:00
10:30	10:30	10:30	10:30
11:00	11:00	11:00	11:00

( )	( )	( )	( )

WEEKLY REFLECTION

....

1) What was my greatest accomplishment this week?

2) Who or what am I grateful for?

3) What activity from this last week took away from my focus and time?

4) What is one thing I can do to be better prepared for this week?

5) What am I looking forward to during the upcoming week?

BRAINSTORM

FINANCIAL CHECKBOX

Questions	Yes	No
Did I remain on budget this week?		
Did I buy what I needed over what I wanted?		
If you got paid this week, did you place 10% of it in your savings?		
Have I taken a percentage (1%-10%) to donate?		
Did I use my credit card wisely this week?		

How can I manage my money more wisely this week?

MONTHLY REFLECTION

· ·

Write 5 things you accomplished this month:

1.

2.

3.

4.

5.

QUESTIONS

1) What did I learn about myself this month?

2) What tasks are left over from this month that are lingering and need to get done?

3. Did I take care of myself?

4) What could I have done differently this past month?

5) What areas can I (still) improve on?

6) What experiences can I treasure?

7) What challenged me and how did I overcome the challenge?

8) What specific habits and/or rituals could I develop this month to support my vision?

MONTH OF:	SUNDAY	MONDAY	TUESDAY
This Month's Goal			
Important Events or Reminders to Transfer to My Phone			
1.			
2.			
3.			
4.			
5.			
6.			
7.			
8.			
9.			
10.			

PROJECT NAME	CLASS & INSTRUCTOR	IMPORTANT DATES	DEADLINES
1.			
2.			
3.			
4.			

WEDNESDAY	THURSDAY	FRIDAY	SATURDAY

BRAINSTORM

Week of:		Sunday		Monday		Tuesday	
This Week's Goal		S		S		S	
		A		A		A	
		V		V		V	
		E		E		E	
		R		R		R	
		S		S		S	
Intention for the Day		◆		◆		◆	
Grateful for ...		◆		◆		◆	

Two roads diverged in a wood, and I—I took the one less traveled by, And that has made all the difference.

—ROBERT FROST

TO-DO LIST	Sunday	Monday	Tuesday
Highest Priority	5:00	5:00	5:00
	5:30	5:30	5:30
	6:00	6:00	6:00
	6:30	6:30	6:30
	7:00	7:00	7:00
	7:30	7:30	7:30
	8:00	8:00	8:00
	8:30	8:30	8:30
	9:00	9:00	9:00
	9:30	9:30	9:30
	10:00	10:00	10:00
	10:30	10:30	10:30
	11:00	11:00	11:00
	11:30	11:30	11:30
	12:00	12:00	12:00
	12:30	12:30	12:30
	1:00	1:00	1:00
Definite Priority	1:30	1:30	1:30
	2:00	2:00	2:00
	2:30	2:30	2:30
	3:00	3:00	3:00
	3:30	3:30	3:30
	4:00	4:00	4:00
Lowest Priority	4:30	4:30	4:30
	5:00	5:00	5:00
	5:30	5:30	5:30
	6:00	6:00	6:00
	6:30	6:30	6:30
	7:00	7:00	7:00
	7:30	7:30	7:30
Habit to Work on This Week	8:00	8:00	8:00
	8:30	8:30	8:30
	9:00	9:00	9:00
	9:30	9:30	9:30
	10:00	10:00	10:00
	10:30	10:30	10:30
	11:00	11:00	11:00

Ready for tomorrow?	( )	( )	( )
ALARM			
CLOTHES/BACKPACK			
GLASS OF WATER			
SAVERS PREP			
BEDTIME AFFIRMATIONS			

Wednesday	Thursday	Friday	Saturday
S	S	S	S
A	A	A	A
V	V	V	V
E	E	E	E
R	R	R	R
S	S	S	S
◆	◆	◆	◆
◆	◆	◆	◆

Wednesday		Thursday		Friday		Saturday	
5:00		5:00		5:00		5:00	
5:30		5:30		5:30		5:30	
6:00		6:00		6:00		6:00	
6:30		6:30		6:30		6:30	
7:00		7:00		7:00		7:00	
7:30		7:30		7:30		7:30	
8:00		8:00		8:00		8:00	
8:30		8:30		8:30		8:30	
9:00		9:00		9:00		9:00	
9:30		9:30		9:30		9:30	
10:00		10:00		10:00		10:00	
10:30		10:30		10:30		10:30	
11:00		11:00		11:00		11:00	
11:30		11:30		11:30		11:30	
12:00		12:00		12:00		12:00	
12:30		12:30		12:30		12:30	
1:00		1:00		1:00		1:00	
1:30		1:30		1:30		1:30	
2:00		2:00		2:00		2:00	
2:30		2:30		2:30		2:30	
3:00		3:00		3:00		3:00	
3:30		3:30		3:30		3:30	
4:00		4:00		4:00		4:00	
4:30		4:30		4:30		4:30	
5:00		5:00		5:00		5:00	
5:30		5:30		5:30		5:30	
6:00		6:00		6:00		6:00	
6:30		6:30		6:30		6:30	
7:00		7:00		7:00		7:00	
7:30		7:30		7:30		7:30	
8:00		8:00		8:00		8:00	
8:30		8:30		8:30		8:30	
9:00		9:00		9:00		9:00	
9:30		9:30		9:30		9:30	
10:00		10:00		10:00		10:00	
10:30		10:30		10:30		10:30	
11:00		11:00		11:00		11:00	

( )	( )	( )	( )

WEEKLY REFLECTION

. . . .

1) What was my greatest accomplishment this week?

2) Who or what am I grateful for?

3) What activity from this last week took away from my focus and time?

4) What is one thing I can do to be better prepared for this week?

5) What am I looking forward to during the upcoming week?

BRAINSTORM

FINANCIAL CHECKBOX

Questions	Yes	No
Did I remain on budget this week?		
Did I buy what I needed over what I wanted?		
If you got paid this week, did you place 10% of it in your savings?		
Have I taken a percentage (1%-10%) to donate?		
Did I use my credit card wisely this week?		
How can I manage my money more wisely this week?		

Week of:	Sunday	Monday	Tuesday
This Week's Goal	S	S	S
	A	A	A
	V	V	V
	E	E	E
	R	R	R
	S	S	S
Intention for the Day	◆	◆	◆
Grateful for ...	◆	◆	◆

Give up being perfect for being authentic.

—HAL ELROD

TO-DO LIST

Highest Priority

Definite Priority

Lowest Priority

Habit to Work on This Week

	Sunday	Monday	Tuesday
5:00		5:00		5:00	
5:30		5:30		5:30	
6:00		6:00		6:00	
6:30		6:30		6:30	
7:00		7:00		7:00	
7:30		7:30		7:30	
8:00		8:00		8:00	
8:30		8:30		8:30	
9:00		9:00		9:00	
9:30		9:30		9:30	
10:00		10:00		10:00	
10:30		10:30		10:30	
11:00		11:00		11:00	
11:30		11:30		11:30	
12:00		12:00		12:00	
12:30		12:30		12:30	
1:00		1:00		1:00	
1:30		1:30		1:30	
2:00		2:00		2:00	
2:30		2:30		2:30	
3:00		3:00		3:00	
3:30		3:30		3:30	
4:00		4:00		4:00	
4:30		4:30		4:30	
5:00		5:00		5:00	
5:30		5:30		5:30	
6:00		6:00		6:00	
6:30		6:30		6:30	
7:00		7:00		7:00	
7:30		7:30		7:30	
8:00		8:00		8:00	
8:30		8:30		8:30	
9:00		9:00		9:00	
9:30		9:30		9:30	
10:00		10:00		10:00	
10:30		10:30		10:30	
11:00		11:00		11:00	

Ready for tomorrow?	( )	( )	( )
ALARM			
CLOTHES/BACKPACK			
GLASS OF WATER			
SAVERS PREP			
BEDTIME AFFIRMATIONS			

Wednesday	Thursday	Friday	Saturday
S	S	S	S
A	A	A	A
V	V	V	V
E	E	E	E
R	R	R	R
S	S	S	S
◆	◆	◆	◆
◆	◆	◆	◆

Wednesday	Thursday	Friday	Saturday
5:00	5:00	5:00	5:00
5:30	5:30	5:30	5:30
6:00	6:00	6:00	6:00
6:30	6:30	6:30	6:30
7:00	7:00	7:00	7:00
7:30	7:30	7:30	7:30
8:00	8:00	8:00	8:00
8:30	8:30	8:30	8:30
9:00	9:00	9:00	9:00
9:30	9:30	9:30	9:30
10:00	10:00	10:00	10:00
10:30	10:30	10:30	10:30
11:00	11:00	11:00	11:00
11:30	11:30	11:30	11:30
12:00	12:00	12:00	12:00
12:30	12:30	12:30	12:30
1:00	1:00	1:00	1:00
1:30	1:30	1:30	1:30
2:00	2:00	2:00	2:00
2:30	2:30	2:30	2:30
3:00	3:00	3:00	3:00
3:30	3:30	3:30	3:30
4:00	4:00	4:00	4:00
4:30	4:30	4:30	4:30
5:00	5:00	5:00	5:00
5:30	5:30	5:30	5:30
6:00	6:00	6:00	6:00
6:30	6:30	6:30	6:30
7:00	7:00	7:00	7:00
7:30	7:30	7:30	7:30
8:00	8:00	8:00	8:00
8:30	8:30	8:30	8:30
9:00	9:00	9:00	9:00
9:30	9:30	9:30	9:30
10:00	10:00	10:00	10:00
10:30	10:30	10:30	10:30
11:00	11:00	11:00	11:00

( )	( )	( )	( )

WEEKLY REFLECTION

• •

1) What was my greatest accomplishment this week?

2) Who or what am I grateful for?

3) What activity from this last week took away from my focus and time?

4) What is one thing I can do to be better prepared for this week?

5) What am I looking forward to during the upcoming week?

BRAINSTORM

FINANCIAL CHECKBOX

Questions	Yes	No
Did I remain on budget this week?		
Did I buy what I needed over what I wanted?		
If you got paid this week, did you place 10% of it in your savings?		
Have I taken a percentage (1%-10%) to donate?		
Did I use my credit card wisely this week?		

How can I manage my money more wisely this week?

Week of:	Sunday	Monday	Tuesday
This Week's Goal	S	S	S
	A	A	A
	V	V	V
	E	E	E
	R	R	R
	S	S	S
Intention for the Day	◆	◆	◆
Grateful for ...	◆	◆	◆

When one door of happiness closes, another opens, but often we look so long at the closed door that we do not see the one that has been opened for us.

—HELEN KELLER

TO-DO LIST	Sunday	Monday	Tuesday
Highest Priority	5:00	5:00	5:00
	5:30	5:30	5:30
	6:00	6:00	6:00
	6:30	6:30	6:30
	7:00	7:00	7:00
	7:30	7:30	7:30
	8:00	8:00	8:00
	8:30	8:30	8:30
	9:00	9:00	9:00
	9:30	9:30	9:30
	10:00	10:00	10:00
	10:30	10:30	10:30
	11:00	11:00	11:00
	11:30	11:30	11:30
	12:00	12:00	12:00
	12:30	12:30	12:30
	1:00	1:00	1:00
Definite Priority	1:30	1:30	1:30
	2:00	2:00	2:00
	2:30	2:30	2:30
	3:00	3:00	3:00
	3:30	3:30	3:30
	4:00	4:00	4:00
Lowest Priority	4:30	4:30	4:30
	5:00	5:00	5:00
	5:30	5:30	5:30
	6:00	6:00	6:00
	6:30	6:30	6:30
	7:00	7:00	7:00
	7:30	7:30	7:30
Habit to Work on This Week	8:00	8:00	8:00
	8:30	8:30	8:30
	9:00	9:00	9:00
	9:30	9:30	9:30
	10:00	10:00	10:00
	10:30	10:30	10:30
	11:00	11:00	11:00

Ready for tomorrow?	( )	( )	( )
ALARM			
CLOTHES/BACKPACK			
GLASS OF WATER			
SAVERS PREP			
BEDTIME AFFIRMATIONS			

Wednesday	Thursday	Friday	Saturday
S	S	S	S
A	A	A	A
V	V	V	V
E	E	E	E
R	R	R	R
S	S	S	S
◆	◆	◆	◆
◆	◆	◆	◆

Wednesday		Thursday		Friday		Saturday	
5:00		5:00		5:00		5:00	
5:30		5:30		5:30		5:30	
6:00		6:00		6:00		6:00	
6:30		6:30		6:30		6:30	
7:00		7:00		7:00		7:00	
7:30		7:30		7:30		7:30	
8:00		8:00		8:00		8:00	
8:30		8:30		8:30		8:30	
9:00		9:00		9:00		9:00	
9:30		9:30		9:30		9:30	
10:00		10:00		10:00		10:00	
10:30		10:30		10:30		10:30	
11:00		11:00		11:00		11:00	
11:30		11:30		11:30		11:30	
12:00		12:00		12:00		12:00	
12:30		12:30		12:30		12:30	
1:00		1:00		1:00		1:00	
1:30		1:30		1:30		1:30	
2:00		2:00		2:00		2:00	
2:30		2:30		2:30		2:30	
3:00		3:00		3:00		3:00	
3:30		3:30		3:30		3:30	
4:00		4:00		4:00		4:00	
4:30		4:30		4:30		4:30	
5:00		5:00		5:00		5:00	
5:30		5:30		5:30		5:30	
6:00		6:00		6:00		6:00	
6:30		6:30		6:30		6:30	
7:00		7:00		7:00		7:00	
7:30		7:30		7:30		7:30	
8:00		8:00		8:00		8:00	
8:30		8:30		8:30		8:30	
9:00		9:00		9:00		9:00	
9:30		9:30		9:30		9:30	
10:00		10:00		10:00		10:00	
10:30		10:30		10:30		10:30	
11:00		11:00		11:00			

( )	( )	( )	( )

WEEKLY REFLECTION

• •

1) What was my greatest accomplishment this week?

2) Who or what am I grateful for?

3) What activity from this last week took away from my focus and time?

4) What is one thing I can do to be better prepared for this week?

5) What am I looking forward to during the upcoming week?

BRAINSTORM

FINANCIAL CHECKBOX

Questions	Yes	No
Did I remain on budget this week?		
Did I buy what I needed over what I wanted?		
If you got paid this week, did you place 10% of it in your savings?		
Have I taken a percentage (1%-10%) to donate?		
Did I use my credit card wisely this week?		

How can I manage my money more wisely this week?

Week of:	Sunday		Monday		Tuesday	
This Week's Goal	S		S		S	
	A		A		A	
	V		V		V	
	E		E		E	
	R		R		R	
	S		S		S	
Intention for the Day	◆		◆		◆	
Grateful for ...	◆		◆		◆	

> *Success is something you attract by the person you become.*
>
> **—JIM ROHN**

	Sunday	Monday	Tuesday
TO-DO LIST	5:00	5:00	5:00
Highest Priority	5:30	5:30	5:30
	6:00	6:00	6:00
	6:30	6:30	6:30
	7:00	7:00	7:00
	7:30	7:30	7:30
	8:00	8:00	8:00
	8:30	8:30	8:30
	9:00	9:00	9:00
	9:30	9:30	9:30
	10:00	10:00	10:00
	10:30	10:30	10:30
	11:00	11:00	11:00
	11:30	11:30	11:30
	12:00	12:00	12:00
	12:30	12:30	12:30
	1:00	1:00	1:00
Definite Priority	1:30	1:30	1:30
	2:00	2:00	2:00
	2:30	2:30	2:30
	3:00	3:00	3:00
	3:30	3:30	3:30
	4:00	4:00	4:00
Lowest Priority	4:30	4:30	4:30
	5:00	5:00	5:00
	5:30	5:30	5:30
	6:00	6:00	6:00
	6:30	6:30	6:30
	7:00	7:00	7:00
	7:30	7:30	7:30
Habit to Work on This Week	8:00	8:00	8:00
	8:30	8:30	8:30
	9:00	9:00	9:00
	9:30	9:30	9:30
	10:00	10:00	10:00
	10:30	10:30	10:30
	11:00	11:00	11:00

Ready for tomorrow?	( )	( )	( )
ALARM			
CLOTHES/BACKPACK			
GLASS OF WATER			
SAVERS PREP			
BEDTIME AFFIRMATIONS			

Wednesday	Thursday	Friday	Saturday
S	S	S	S
A	A	A	A
V	V	V	V
E	E	E	E
R	R	R	R
S	S	S	S

◆	◆	◆	◆
◆	◆	◆	◆

Wednesday	Thursday	Friday	Saturday
5:00	5:00	5:00	5:00
5:30	5:30	5:30	5:30
6:00	6:00	6:00	6:00
6:30	6:30	6:30	6:30
7:00	7:00	7:00	7:00
7:30	7:30	7:30	7:30
8:00	8:00	8:00	8:00
8:30	8:30	8:30	8:30
9:00	9:00	9:00	9:00
9:30	9:30	9:30	9:30
10:00	10:00	10:00	10:00
10:30	10:30	10:30	10:30
11:00	11:00	11:00	11:00
11:30	11:30	11:30	11:30
12:00	12:00	12:00	12:00
12:30	12:30	12:30	12:30
1:00	1:00	1:00	1:00
1:30	1:30	1:30	1:30
2:00	2:00	2:00	2:00
2:30	2:30	2:30	2:30
3:00	3:00	3:00	3:00
3:30	3:30	3:30	3:30
4:00	4:00	4:00	4:00
4:30	4:30	4:30	4:30
5:00	5:00	5:00	5:00
5:30	5:30	5:30	5:30
6:00	6:00	6:00	6:00
6:30	6:30	6:30	6:30
7:00	7:00	7:00	7:00
7:30	7:30	7:30	7:30
8:00	8:00	8:00	8:00
8:30	8:30	8:30	8:30
9:00	9:00	9:00	9:00
9:30	9:30	9:30	9:30
10:00	10:00	10:00	10:00
10:30	10:30	10:30	10:30
11:00	11:00	11:00	11:00

( )	( )	( )	( )

WEEKLY REFLECTION

. . . .

1) What was my greatest accomplishment this week?

2) Who or what am I grateful for?

3) What activity from this last week took away from my focus and time?

4) What is one thing I can do to be better prepared for this week?

5) What am I looking forward to during the upcoming week?

BRAINSTORM

FINANCIAL CHECKBOX

Questions	Yes	No
Did I remain on budget this week?		
Did I buy what I needed over what I wanted?		
If you got paid this week, did you place 10% of it in your savings?		
Have I taken a percentage (1%-10%) to donate?		
Did I use my credit card wisely this week?		
How can I manage my money more wisely this week?		

Week of:		Sunday		Monday		Tuesday
This Week's Goal		S		S		S
		A		A		A
		V		V		V
		E		E		E
		R		R		R
		S		S		S
Intention for the Day		◆		◆		◆
Grateful for ...		◆		◆		◆

Start where you are.
Use what you have.
Do what you can.

—ARTHUR ASHE

TO-DO LIST

Highest Priority

Definite Priority

Lowest Priority

Habit to Work on This Week

	Sunday	Monday	Tuesday
5:00		5:00	5:00
5:30		5:30	5:30
6:00		6:00	6:00
6:30		6:30	6:30
7:00		7:00	7:00
7:30		7:30	7:30
8:00		8:00	8:00
8:30		8:30	8:30
9:00		9:00	9:00
9:30		9:30	9:30
10:00		10:00	10:00
10:30		10:30	10:30
11:00		11:00	11:00
11:30		11:30	11:30
12:00		12:00	12:00
12:30		12:30	12:30
1:00		1:00	1:00
1:30		1:30	1:30
2:00		2:00	2:00
2:30		2:30	2:30
3:00		3:00	3:00
3:30		3:30	3:30
4:00		4:00	4:00
4:30		4:30	4:30
5:00		5:00	5:00
5:30		5:30	5:30
6:00		6:00	6:00
6:30		6:30	6:30
7:00		7:00	7:00
7:30		7:30	7:30
8:00		8:00	8:00
8:30		8:30	8:30
9:00		9:00	9:00
9:30		9:30	9:30
10:00		10:00	10:00
10:30		10:30	10:30
11:00		11:00	11:00

Ready for tomorrow?		( )		( )		( )
ALARM						
CLOTHES/BACKPACK						
GLASS OF WATER						
SAVERS PREP						
BEDTIME AFFIRMATIONS						

Wednesday	Thursday	Friday	Saturday
S	S	S	S
A	A	A	A
V	V	V	V
E	E	E	E
R	R	R	R
S	S	S	S
◆	◆	◆	◆
◆	◆	◆	◆

Wednesday	Thursday	Friday	Saturday
5:00	5:00	5:00	5:00
5:30	5:30	5:30	5:30
6:00	6:00	6:00	6:00
6:30	6:30	6:30	6:30
7:00	7:00	7:00	7:00
7:30	7:30	7:30	7:30
8:00	8:00	8:00	8:00
8:30	8:30	8:30	8:30
9:00	9:00	9:00	9:00
9:30	9:30	9:30	9:30
10:00	10:00	10:00	10:00
10:30	10:30	10:30	10:30
11:00	11:00	11:00	11:00
11:30	11:30	11:30	11:30
12:00	12:00	12:00	12:00
12:30	12:30	12:30	12:30
1:00	1:00	1:00	1:00
1:30	1:30	1:30	1:30
2:00	2:00	2:00	2:00
2:30	2:30	2:30	2:30
3:00	3:00	3:00	3:00
3:30	3:30	3:30	3:30
4:00	4:00	4:00	4:00
4:30	4:30	4:30	4:30
5:00	5:00	5:00	5:00
5:30	5:30	5:30	5:30
6:00	6:00	6:00	6:00
6:30	6:30	6:30	6:30
7:00	7:00	7:00	7:00
7:30	7:30	7:30	7:30
8:00	8:00	8:00	8:00
8:30	8:30	8:30	8:30
9:00	9:00	9:00	9:00
9:30	9:30	9:30	9:30
10:00	10:00	10:00	10:00
10:30	10:30	10:30	10:30
11:00	11:00	11:00	11:00
( )	( )	( )	( )

WEEKLY REFLECTION

. . . .

1) What was my greatest accomplishment this week?

2) Who or what am I grateful for?

3) What activity from this last week took away from my focus and time?

4) What is one thing I can do to be better prepared for this week?

5) What am I looking forward to during the upcoming week?

BRAINSTORM

FINANCIAL CHECKBOX

Questions	Yes	No
Did I remain on budget this week?		
Did I buy what I needed over what I wanted?		
If you got paid this week, did you place 10% of it in your savings?		
Have I taken a percentage (1%-10%) to donate?		
Did I use my credit card wisely this week?		
How can I manage my money more wisely this week?		

MONTHLY REFLECTION

· ·

Write 5 things you accomplished this month:

1.

2.

3.

4.

5.

QUESTIONS

1) What did I learn about myself this month?

2) What tasks are left over from this month that are lingering and need to get done?

3. Did I take care of myself?

4) What could I have done differently this past month?

5) What areas can I (still) improve on?

6) What experiences can I treasure?

7) What challenged me and how did I overcome the challenge?

8) What specific habits and/or rituals could I develop this month to support my vision?

MONTH OF:	SUNDAY	MONDAY	TUESDAY
This Month's Goal			
Important Events or Reminders to Transfer to My Phone			
1.			
2.			
3.			
4.			
5.			
6.			
7.			
8.			
9.			
10.			

PROJECT NAME	CLASS & INSTRUCTOR	IMPORTANT DATES	DEADLINES
1.			
2.			
3.			
4.			

WEDNESDAY	THURSDAY	FRIDAY	SATURDAY

BRAINSTORM

Week of:	Sunday		Monday		Tuesday	
This Week's Goal	S		S		S	
	A		A		A	
	V		V		V	
	E		E		E	
	R		R		R	
	S		S		S	
Intention for the Day	◆		◆		◆	
Grateful for ...	◆		◆		◆	

Certain things catch your eye, but pursue only those that capture the heart.

—ANCIENT INDIAN PROVERB

TO-DO LIST
Highest Priority
Definite Priority
Lowest Priority
Habit to Work on This Week

Sunday	Monday	Tuesday
5:00	5:00	5:00
5:30	5:30	5:30
6:00	6:00	6:00
6:30	6:30	6:30
7:00	7:00	7:00
7:30	7:30	7:30
8:00	8:00	8:00
8:30	8:30	8:30
9:00	9:00	9:00
9:30	9:30	9:30
10:00	10:00	10:00
10:30	10:30	10:30
11:00	11:00	11:00
11:30	11:30	11:30
12:00	12:00	12:00
12:30	12:30	12:30
1:00	1:00	1:00
1:30	1:30	1:30
2:00	2:00	2:00
2:30	2:30	2:30
3:00	3:00	3:00
3:30	3:30	3:30
4:00	4:00	4:00
4:30	4:30	4:30
5:00	5:00	5:00
5:30	5:30	5:30
6:00	6:00	6:00
6:30	6:30	6:30
7:00	7:00	7:00
7:30	7:30	7:30
8:00	8:00	8:00
8:30	8:30	8:30
9:00	9:00	9:00
9:30	9:30	9:30
10:00	10:00	10:00
10:30	10:30	10:30
11:00	11:00	11:00

Ready for tomorrow?	( )	( )	( )
ALARM			
CLOTHES/BACKPACK			
GLASS OF WATER			
SAVERS PREP			
BEDTIME AFFIRMATIONS			

Wednesday	Thursday	Friday	Saturday
S	S	S	S
A	A	A	A
V	V	V	V
E	E	E	E
R	R	R	R
S	S	S	S
◆	◆	◆	◆
◆	◆	◆	◆

Wednesday		Thursday		Friday		Saturday	
5:00		5:00		5:00		5:00	
5:30		5:30		5:30		5:30	
6:00		6:00		6:00		6:00	
6:30		6:30		6:30		6:30	
7:00		7:00		7:00		7:00	
7:30		7:30		7:30		7:30	
8:00		8:00		8:00		8:00	
8:30		8:30		8:30		8:30	
9:00		9:00		9:00		9:00	
9:30		9:30		9:30		9:30	
10:00		10:00		10:00		10:00	
10:30		10:30		10:30		10:30	
11:00		11:00		11:00		11:00	
11:30		11:30		11:30		11:30	
12:00		12:00		12:00		12:00	
12:30		12:30		12:30		12:30	
1:00		1:00		1:00		1:00	
1:30		1:30		1:30		1:30	
2:00		2:00		2:00		2:00	
2:30		2:30		2:30		2:30	
3:00		3:00		3:00		3:00	
3:30		3:30		3:30		3:30	
4:00		4:00		4:00		4:00	
4:30		4:30		4:30		4:30	
5:00		5:00		5:00		5:00	
5:30		5:30		5:30		5:30	
6:00		6:00		6:00		6:00	
6:30		6:30		6:30		6:30	
7:00		7:00		7:00		7:00	
7:30		7:30		7:30		7:30	
8:00		8:00		8:00		8:00	
8:30		8:30		8:30		8:30	
9:00		9:00		9:00		9:00	
9:30		9:30		9:30		9:30	
10:00		10:00		10:00		10:00	
10:30		10:30		10:30		10:30	
11:00		11:00		11:00		11:00	
	( )		( )		( )		( )

WEEKLY REFLECTION

• •

1) What was my greatest accomplishment this week?

2) Who or what am I grateful for?

3) What activity from this last week took away from my focus and time?

4) What is one thing I can do to be better prepared for this week?

5) What am I looking forward to during the upcoming week?

BRAINSTORM

FINANCIAL CHECKBOX

Questions	Yes	No
Did I remain on budget this week?		
Did I buy what I needed over what I wanted?		
If you got paid this week, did you place 10% of it in your savings?		
Have I taken a percentage (1%-10%) to donate?		
Did I use my credit card wisely this week?		
How can I manage my money more wisely this week?		

Week of:	Sunday	Monday	Tuesday
This Week's Goal	S	S	S
	A	A	A
	V	V	V
	E	E	E
	R	R	R
	S	S	S
Intention for the Day	◆	◆	◆
Grateful for …	◆	◆	◆

Your success is someone else's miracle.

—JEFF HOFFMAN

TO-DO LIST
Highest Priority
Definite Priority
Lowest Priority
Habit to Work on This Week

	Sunday	Monday	Tuesday
5:00			
5:30			
6:00			
6:30			
7:00			
7:30			
8:00			
8:30			
9:00			
9:30			
10:00			
10:30			
11:00			
11:30			
12:00			
12:30			
1:00			
1:30			
2:00			
2:30			
3:00			
3:30			
4:00			
4:30			
5:00			
5:30			
6:00			
6:30			
7:00			
7:30			
8:00			
8:30			
9:00			
9:30			
10:00			
10:30			
11:00			

Ready for tomorrow?	( )	( )	( )
ALARM			
CLOTHES/BACKPACK			
GLASS OF WATER			
SAVERS PREP			
BEDTIME AFFIRMATIONS			

Wednesday		Thursday		Friday		Saturday	
S		S		S		S	
A		A		A		A	
V		V		V		V	
E		E		E		E	
R		R		R		R	
S		S		S		S	
◆		◆		◆		◆	
◆		◆		◆		◆	
5:00		5:00		5:00		5:00	
5:30		5:30		5:30		5:30	
6:00		6:00		6:00		6:00	
6:30		6:30		6:30		6:30	
7:00		7:00		7:00		7:00	
7:30		7:30		7:30		7:30	
8:00		8:00		8:00		8:00	
8:30		8:30		8:30		8:30	
9:00		9:00		9:00		9:00	
9:30		9:30		9:30		9:30	
10:00		10:00		10:00		10:00	
10:30		10:30		10:30		10:30	
11:00		11:00		11:00		11:00	
11:30		11:30		11:30		11:30	
12:00		12:00		12:00		12:00	
12:30		12:30		12:30		12:30	
1:00		1:00		1:00		1:00	
1:30		1:30		1:30		1:30	
2:00		2:00		2:00		2:00	
2:30		2:30		2:30		2:30	
3:00		3:00		3:00		3:00	
3:30		3:30		3:30		3:30	
4:00		4:00		4:00		4:00	
4:30		4:30		4:30		4:30	
5:00		5:00		5:00		5:00	
5:30		5:30		5:30		5:30	
6:00		6:00		6:00		6:00	
6:30		6:30		6:30		6:30	
7:00		7:00		7:00		7:00	
7:30		7:30		7:30		7:30	
8:00		8:00		8:00		8:00	
8:30		8:30		8:30		8:30	
9:00		9:00		9:00		9:00	
9:30		9:30		9:30		9:30	
10:00		10:00		10:00		10:00	
10:30		10:30		10:30		10:30	
11:00		11:00		11:00		11:00	
	( )		( )		( )		( )

WEEKLY REFLECTION

• •

1)   What was my greatest accomplishment this week?

2)   Who or what am I grateful for?

3)   What activity from this last week took away from my focus and time?

4)   What is one thing I can do to be better prepared for this week?

5)   What am I looking forward to during the upcoming week?

BRAINSTORM

FINANCIAL CHECKBOX

Questions	Yes	No
Did I remain on budget this week?		
Did I buy what I needed over what I wanted?		
If you got paid this week, did you place 10% of it in your savings?		
Have I taken a percentage (1%-10%) to donate?		
Did I use my credit card wisely this week?		
How can I manage my money more wisely this week?		

Week of:	Sunday	Monday	Tuesday
This Week's Goal	S	S	S
	A	A	A
	V	V	V
	E	E	E
	R	R	R
	S	S	S
Intention for the Day	◆	◆	◆
Grateful for ...	◆	◆	◆

Anyone who has never made a mistake has never tried anything new.

—ALBERT EINSTEIN

TO-DO LIST	Sunday	Monday	Tuesday
Highest Priority	5:00	5:00	5:00
	5:30	5:30	5:30
	6:00	6:00	6:00
	6:30	6:30	6:30
	7:00	7:00	7:00
	7:30	7:30	7:30
	8:00	8:00	8:00
	8:30	8:30	8:30
	9:00	9:00	9:00
	9:30	9:30	9:30
	10:00	10:00	10:00
	10:30	10:30	10:30
	11:00	11:00	11:00
	11:30	11:30	11:30
	12:00	12:00	12:00
	12:30	12:30	12:30
	1:00	1:00	1:00
Definite Priority	1:30	1:30	1:30
	2:00	2:00	2:00
	2:30	2:30	2:30
	3:00	3:00	3:00
	3:30	3:30	3:30
	4:00	4:00	4:00
Lowest Priority	4:30	4:30	4:30
	5:00	5:00	5:00
	5:30	5:30	5:30
	6:00	6:00	6:00
	6:30	6:30	6:30
	7:00	7:00	7:00
	7:30	7:30	7:30
Habit to Work on This Week	8:00	8:00	8:00
	8:30	8:30	8:30
	9:00	9:00	9:00
	9:30	9:30	9:30
	10:00	10:00	10:00
	10:30	10:30	10:30
	11:00	11:00	11:00

Ready for tomorrow?	( )	( )	( )
ALARM			
CLOTHES/BACKPACK			
GLASS OF WATER			
SAVERS PREP			
BEDTIME AFFIRMATIONS			

Wednesday		Thursday		Friday		Saturday	
S		S		S		S	
A		A		A		A	
V		V		V		V	
E		E		E		E	
R		R		R		R	
S		S		S		S	
◆		◆		◆		◆	
◆		◆		◆		◆	
5:00		5:00		5:00		5:00	
5:30		5:30		5:30		5:30	
6:00		6:00		6:00		6:00	
6:30		6:30		6:30		6:30	
7:00		7:00		7:00		7:00	
7:30		7:30		7:30		7:30	
8:00		8:00		8:00		8:00	
8:30		8:30		8:30		8:30	
9:00		9:00		9:00		9:00	
9:30		9:30		9:30		9:30	
10:00		10:00		10:00		10:00	
10:30		10:30		10:30		10:30	
11:00		11:00		11:00		11:00	
11:30		11:30		11:30		11:30	
12:00		12:00		12:00		12:00	
12:30		12:30		12:30		12:30	
1:00		1:00		1:00		1:00	
1:30		1:30		1:30		1:30	
2:00		2:00		2:00		2:00	
2:30		2:30		2:30		2:30	
3:00		3:00		3:00		3:00	
3:30		3:30		3:30		3:30	
4:00		4:00		4:00		4:00	
4:30		4:30		4:30		4:30	
5:00		5:00		5:00		5:00	
5:30		5:30		5:30		5:30	
6:00		6:00		6:00		6:00	
6:30		6:30		6:30		6:30	
7:00		7:00		7:00		7:00	
7:30		7:30		7:30		7:30	
8:00		8:00		8:00		8:00	
8:30		8:30		8:30		8:30	
9:00		9:00		9:00		9:00	
9:30		9:30		9:30		9:30	
10:00		10:00		10:00		10:00	
10:30		10:30		10:30		10:30	
11:00		11:00		11:00		11:00	
	( )		( )		( )		( )

WEEKLY REFLECTION

• •

1) What was my greatest accomplishment this week?

2) Who or what am I grateful for?

3) What activity from this last week took away from my focus and time?

4) What is one thing I can do to be better prepared for this week?

5) What am I looking forward to during the upcoming week?

BRAINSTORM

FINANCIAL CHECKBOX

Questions	Yes	No
Did I remain on budget this week?		
Did I buy what I needed over what I wanted?		
If you got paid this week, did you place 10% of it in your savings?		
Have I taken a percentage (1%-10%) to donate?		
Did I use my credit card wisely this week?		

How can I manage my money more wisely this week?

Week of:	Sunday	Monday	Tuesday
This Week's Goal	S	S	S
	A	A	A
	V	V	V
	E	E	E
	R	R	R
	S	S	S
Intention for the Day	◆	◆	◆
Grateful for ...	◆	◆	◆

Make each day your masterpiece.

—JOHN WOODEN

TO-DO LIST	Sunday	Monday	Tuesday
Highest Priority	5:00	5:00	5:00
	5:30	5:30	5:30
	6:00	6:00	6:00
	6:30	6:30	6:30
	7:00	7:00	7:00
	7:30	7:30	7:30
	8:00	8:00	8:00
	8:30	8:30	8:30
	9:00	9:00	9:00
	9:30	9:30	9:30
	10:00	10:00	10:00
	10:30	10:30	10:30
	11:00	11:00	11:00
	11:30	11:30	11:30
	12:00	12:00	12:00
	12:30	12:30	12:30
	1:00	1:00	1:00
Definite Priority	1:30	1:30	1:30
	2:00	2:00	2:00
	2:30	2:30	2:30
	3:00	3:00	3:00
	3:30	3:30	3:30
	4:00	4:00	4:00
Lowest Priority	4:30	4:30	4:30
	5:00	5:00	5:00
	5:30	5:30	5:30
	6:00	6:00	6:00
	6:30	6:30	6:30
	7:00	7:00	7:00
	7:30	7:30	7:30
Habit to Work on This Week	8:00	8:00	8:00
	8:30	8:30	8:30
	9:00	9:00	9:00
	9:30	9:30	9:30
	10:00	10:00	10:00
	10:30	10:30	10:30
	11:00	11:00	11:00

Ready for tomorrow?	( )	( )	( )
ALARM			
CLOTHES/BACKPACK			
GLASS OF WATER			
SAVERS PREP			
BEDTIME AFFIRMATIONS			

Wednesday		Thursday		Friday		Saturday	
S		S		S		S	
A		A		A		A	
V		V		V		V	
E		E		E		E	
R		R		R		R	
S		S		S		S	
◆		◆		◆		◆	
◆		◆		◆		◆	
5:00		5:00		5:00		5:00	
5:30		5:30		5:30		5:30	
6:00		6:00		6:00		6:00	
6:30		6:30		6:30		6:30	
7:00		7:00		7:00		7:00	
7:30		7:30		7:30		7:30	
8:00		8:00		8:00		8:00	
8:30		8:30		8:30		8:30	
9:00		9:00		9:00		9:00	
9:30		9:30		9:30		9:30	
10:00		10:00		10:00		10:00	
10:30		10:30		10:30		10:30	
11:00		11:00		11:00		11:00	
11:30		11:30		11:30		11:30	
12:00		12:00		12:00		12:00	
12:30		12:30		12:30		12:30	
1:00		1:00		1:00		1:00	
1:30		1:30		1:30		1:30	
2:00		2:00		2:00		2:00	
2:30		2:30		2:30		2:30	
3:00		3:00		3:00		3:00	
3:30		3:30		3:30		3:30	
4:00		4:00		4:00		4:00	
4:30		4:30		4:30		4:30	
5:00		5:00		5:00		5:00	
5:30		5:30		5:30		5:30	
6:00		6:00		6:00		6:00	
6:30		6:30		6:30		6:30	
7:00		7:00		7:00		7:00	
7:30		7:30		7:30		7:30	
8:00		8:00		8:00		8:00	
8:30		8:30		8:30		8:30	
9:00		9:00		9:00		9:00	
9:30		9:30		9:30		9:30	
10:00		10:00		10:00		10:00	
10:30		10:30		10:30		10:30	
11:00		11:00		11:00		11:00	
	( )		( )		( )		( )

WEEKLY REFLECTION

• •

1) What was my greatest accomplishment this week?

2) Who or what am I grateful for?

3) What activity from this last week took away from my focus and time?

4) What is one thing I can do to be better prepared for this week?

5) What am I looking forward to during the upcoming week?

BRAINSTORM

FINANCIAL CHECKBOX

Questions	Yes	No
Did I remain on budget this week?		
Did I buy what I needed over what I wanted?		
If you got paid this week, did you place 10% of it in your savings?		
Have I taken a percentage (1%-10%) to donate?		
Did I use my credit card wisely this week?		

How can I manage my money more wisely this week?

Week of:	Sunday		Monday		Tuesday	
This Week's Goal	S		S		S	
	A		A		A	
	V		V		V	
	E		E		E	
	R		R		R	
	S		S		S	
Intention for the Day	◆		◆		◆	
Grateful for ...	◆		◆		◆	

To avoid criticism, do nothing, say nothing, be nothing.

—ELBERT HUBBARD

TO-DO LIST
Highest Priority
Definite Priority
Lowest Priority
Habit to Work on This Week

Time	Sunday	Monday	Tuesday
5:00			
5:30			
6:00			
6:30			
7:00			
7:30			
8:00			
8:30			
9:00			
9:30			
10:00			
10:30			
11:00			
11:30			
12:00			
12:30			
1:00			
1:30			
2:00			
2:30			
3:00			
3:30			
4:00			
4:30			
5:00			
5:30			
6:00			
6:30			
7:00			
7:30			
8:00			
8:30			
9:00			
9:30			
10:00			
10:30			
11:00			

Ready for tomorrow?	( )	( )	( )
ALARM			
CLOTHES/BACKPACK			
GLASS OF WATER			
SAVERS PREP			
BEDTIME AFFIRMATIONS			

Wednesday	Thursday	Friday	Saturday
S	S	S	S
A	A	A	A
V	V	V	V
E	E	E	E
R	R	R	R
S	S	S	S

◆	◆	◆	◆
◆	◆	◆	◆

Wednesday	Thursday	Friday	Saturday
5:00	5:00	5:00	5:00
5:30	5:30	5:30	5:30
6:00	6:00	6:00	6:00
6:30	6:30	6:30	6:30
7:00	7:00	7:00	7:00
7:30	7:30	7:30	7:30
8:00	8:00	8:00	8:00
8:30	8:30	8:30	8:30
9:00	9:00	9:00	9:00
9:30	9:30	9:30	9:30
10:00	10:00	10:00	10:00
10:30	10:30	10:30	10:30
11:00	11:00	11:00	11:00
11:30	11:30	11:30	11:30
12:00	12:00	12:00	12:00
12:30	12:30	12:30	12:30
1:00	1:00	1:00	1:00
1:30	1:30	1:30	1:30
2:00	2:00	2:00	2:00
2:30	2:30	2:30	2:30
3:00	3:00	3:00	3:00
3:30	3:30	3:30	3:30
4:00	4:00	4:00	4:00
4:30	4:30	4:30	4:30
5:00	5:00	5:00	5:00
5:30	5:30	5:30	5:30
6:00	6:00	6:00	6:00
6:30	6:30	6:30	6:30
7:00	7:00	7:00	7:00
7:30	7:30	7:30	7:30
8:00	8:00	8:00	8:00
8:30	8:30	8:30	8:30
9:00	9:00	9:00	9:00
9:30	9:30	9:30	9:30
10:00	10:00	10:00	10:00
10:30	10:30	10:30	10:30
11:00	11:00	11:00	11:00

( )	( )	( )	( )

WEEKLY REFLECTION

• •

1) What was my greatest accomplishment this week?

2) Who or what am I grateful for?

3) What activity from this last week took away from my focus and time?

4) What is one thing I can do to be better prepared for this week?

5) What am I looking forward to during the upcoming week?

BRAINSTORM

FINANCIAL CHECKBOX

Questions	Yes	No
Did I remain on budget this week?		
Did I buy what I needed over what I wanted?		
If you got paid this week, did you place 10% of it in your savings?		
Have I taken a percentage (1%-10%) to donate?		
Did I use my credit card wisely this week?		

How can I manage my money more wisely this week?

MONTHLY REFLECTION

• •

Write 5 things you accomplished this month:

1.

2.

3.

4.

5.

QUESTIONS

1) What did I learn about myself this month?

2) What tasks are left over from this month that are lingering and need to get done?

3. Did I take care of myself?

4) What could I have done differently this past month?

5) What areas can I (still) improve on?

6) What experiences can I treasure?

7) What challenged me and how did I overcome the challenge?

8) What specific habits and/or rituals could I develop this month to support my vision?

MONTH OF:	SUNDAY	MONDAY	TUESDAY
This Month's Goal			
Important Events or Reminders to Transfer to My Phone			
1.			
2.			
3.			
4.			
5.			
6.			
7.			
8.			
9.			
10.			

PROJECT NAME	CLASS & INSTRUCTOR	IMPORTANT DATES	DEADLINES
1.			
2.			
3.			
4.			

WEDNESDAY	THURSDAY	FRIDAY	SATURDAY

BRAINSTORM

Week of:	Sunday	Monday	Tuesday
This Week's Goal	S	S	S
	A	A	A
	V	V	V
	E	E	E
	R	R	R
	S	S	S
Intention for the Day	◆	◆	◆
Grateful for …	◆	◆	◆

It's not whether you get knocked down, it's whether you get up.

—VINCE LOMBARDI

TO-DO LIST	Sunday	Monday	Tuesday
Highest Priority	5:00	5:00	5:00
	5:30	5:30	5:30
	6:00	6:00	6:00
	6:30	6:30	6:30
	7:00	7:00	7:00
	7:30	7:30	7:30
	8:00	8:00	8:00
	8:30	8:30	8:30
	9:00	9:00	9:00
	9:30	9:30	9:30
	10:00	10:00	10:00
	10:30	10:30	10:30
	11:00	11:00	11:00
	11:30	11:30	11:30
	12:00	12:00	12:00
	12:30	12:30	12:30
	1:00	1:00	1:00
Definite Priority	1:30	1:30	1:30
	2:00	2:00	2:00
	2:30	2:30	2:30
	3:00	3:00	3:00
	3:30	3:30	3:30
	4:00	4:00	4:00
Lowest Priority	4:30	4:30	4:30
	5:00	5:00	5:00
	5:30	5:30	5:30
	6:00	6:00	6:00
	6:30	6:30	6:30
	7:00	7:00	7:00
	7:30	7:30	7:30
Habit to Work on This Week	8:00	8:00	8:00
	8:30	8:30	8:30
	9:00	9:00	9:00
	9:30	9:30	9:30
	10:00	10:00	10:00
	10:30	10:30	10:30
	11:00	11:00	11:00

Ready for tomorrow?	( )	( )	( )
ALARM			
CLOTHES/BACKPACK			
GLASS OF WATER			
SAVERS PREP			
BEDTIME AFFIRMATIONS			

Wednesday		Thursday		Friday		Saturday	
S		S		S		S	
A		A		A		A	
V		V		V		V	
E		E		E		E	
R		R		R		R	
S		S		S		S	
◆		◆		◆		◆	
◆		◆		◆		◆	
5:00		5:00		5:00		5:00	
5:30		5:30		5:30		5:30	
6:00		6:00		6:00		6:00	
6:30		6:30		6:30		6:30	
7:00		7:00		7:00		7:00	
7:30		7:30		7:30		7:30	
8:00		8:00		8:00		8:00	
8:30		8:30		8:30		8:30	
9:00		9:00		9:00		9:00	
9:30		9:30		9:30		9:30	
10:00		10:00		10:00		10:00	
10:30		10:30		10:30		10:30	
11:00		11:00		11:00		11:00	
11:30		11:30		11:30		11:30	
12:00		12:00		12:00		12:00	
12:30		12:30		12:30		12:30	
1:00		1:00		1:00		1:00	
1:30		1:30		1:30		1:30	
2:00		2:00		2:00		2:00	
2:30		2:30		2:30		2:30	
3:00		3:00		3:00		3:00	
3:30		3:30		3:30		3:30	
4:00		4:00		4:00		4:00	
4:30		4:30		4:30		4:30	
5:00		5:00		5:00		5:00	
5:30		5:30		5:30		5:30	
6:00		6:00		6:00		6:00	
6:30		6:30		6:30		6:30	
7:00		7:00		7:00		7:00	
7:30		7:30		7:30		7:30	
8:00		8:00		8:00		8:00	
8:30		8:30		8:30		8:30	
9:00		9:00		9:00		9:00	
9:30		9:30		9:30		9:30	
10:00		10:00		10:00		10:00	
10:30		10:30		10:30		10:30	
11:00		11:00		11:00		11:00	
	( )		( )		( )		( )

WEEKLY REFLECTION

....

1) What was my greatest accomplishment this week?

2) Who or what am I grateful for?

3) What activity from this last week took away from my focus and time?

4) What is one thing I can do to be better prepared for this week?

5) What am I looking forward to during the upcoming week?

BRAINSTORM

FINANCIAL CHECKBOX

Questions	Yes	No
Did I remain on budget this week?		
Did I buy what I needed over what I wanted?		
If you got paid this week, did you place 10% of it in your savings?		
Have I taken a percentage (1%-10%) to donate?		
Did I use my credit card wisely this week?		

How can I manage my money more wisely this week?

Week of:	Sunday	Monday	Tuesday
This Week's Goal	S	S	S
	A	A	A
	V	V	V
	E	E	E
	R	R	R
	S	S	S
Intention for the Day	◆	◆	◆
Grateful for ...	◆	◆	◆

There is nothing to fear, because you cannot fail— only learn, grow, and become better than you've ever been before.

—HAL ELROD

TO-DO LIST

Highest Priority

Definite Priority

Lowest Priority

Habit to Work on This Week

Time	Sunday	Monday	Tuesday
5:00			
5:30			
6:00			
6:30			
7:00			
7:30			
8:00			
8:30			
9:00			
9:30			
10:00			
10:30			
11:00			
11:30			
12:00			
12:30			
1:00			
1:30			
2:00			
2:30			
3:00			
3:30			
4:00			
4:30			
5:00			
5:30			
6:00			
6:30			
7:00			
7:30			
8:00			
8:30			
9:00			
9:30			
10:00			
10:30			
11:00			

Ready for tomorrow?	( )	( )	( )
ALARM			
CLOTHES/BACKPACK			
GLASS OF WATER			
SAVERS PREP			
BEDTIME AFFIRMATIONS			

Wednesday	Thursday	Friday	Saturday
S	S	S	S
A	A	A	A
V	V	V	V
E	E	E	E
R	R	R	R
S	S	S	S
◆	◆	◆	◆
◆	◆	◆	◆

Wednesday		Thursday		Friday		Saturday	
5:00		5:00		5:00		5:00	
5:30		5:30		5:30		5:30	
6:00		6:00		6:00		6:00	
6:30		6:30		6:30		6:30	
7:00		7:00		7:00		7:00	
7:30		7:30		7:30		7:30	
8:00		8:00		8:00		8:00	
8:30		8:30		8:30		8:30	
9:00		9:00		9:00		9:00	
9:30		9:30		9:30		9:30	
10:00		10:00		10:00		10:00	
10:30		10:30		10:30		10:30	
11:00		11:00		11:00		11:00	
11:30		11:30		11:30		11:30	
12:00		12:00		12:00		12:00	
12:30		12:30		12:30		12:30	
1:00		1:00		1:00		1:00	
1:30		1:30		1:30		1:30	
2:00		2:00		2:00		2:00	
2:30		2:30		2:30		2:30	
3:00		3:00		3:00		3:00	
3:30		3:30		3:30		3:30	
4:00		4:00		4:00		4:00	
4:30		4:30		4:30		4:30	
5:00		5:00		5:00		5:00	
5:30		5:30		5:30		5:30	
6:00		6:00		6:00		6:00	
6:30		6:30		6:30		6:30	
7:00		7:00		7:00		7:00	
7:30		7:30		7:30		7:30	
8:00		8:00		8:00		8:00	
8:30		8:30		8:30		8:30	
9:00		9:00		9:00		9:00	
9:30		9:30		9:30		9:30	
10:00		10:00		10:00		10:00	
10:30		10:30		10:30		10:30	
11:00		11:00		11:00		11:00	
	( )		( )		( )		( )

WEEKLY REFLECTION

• •

1) What was my greatest accomplishment this week?

2) Who or what am I grateful for?

3) What activity from this last week took away from my focus and time?

4) What is one thing I can do to be better prepared for this week?

5) What am I looking forward to during the upcoming week?

BRAINSTORM

FINANCIAL CHECKBOX

Questions	Yes	No
Did I remain on budget this week?		
Did I buy what I needed over what I wanted?		
If you got paid this week, did you place 10% of it in your savings?		
Have I taken a percentage (1%-10%) to donate?		
Did I use my credit card wisely this week?		

How can I manage my money more wisely this week?

Week of:	Sunday	Monday	Tuesday
This Week's Goal	S	S	S
	A	A	A
	V	V	V
	E	E	E
	R	R	R
	S	S	S
Intention for the Day	◆	◆	◆
Grateful for ...	◆	◆	◆

The harder I work, the luckier I get.

—**GARY PLAYER**

TO-DO LIST

Highest Priority

Definite Priority

Lowest Priority

Habit to Work on This Week

Sunday	Monday	Tuesday
5:00	5:00	5:00
5:30	5:30	5:30
6:00	6:00	6:00
6:30	6:30	6:30
7:00	7:00	7:00
7:30	7:30	7:30
8:00	8:00	8:00
8:30	8:30	8:30
9:00	9:00	9:00
9:30	9:30	9:30
10:00	10:00	10:00
10:30	10:30	10:30
11:00	11:00	11:00
11:30	11:30	11:30
12:00	12:00	12:00
12:30	12:30	12:30
1:00	1:00	1:00
1:30	1:30	1:30
2:00	2:00	2:00
2:30	2:30	2:30
3:00	3:00	3:00
3:30	3:30	3:30
4:00	4:00	4:00
4:30	4:30	4:30
5:00	5:00	5:00
5:30	5:30	5:30
6:00	6:00	6:00
6:30	6:30	6:30
7:00	7:00	7:00
7:30	7:30	7:30
8:00	8:00	8:00
8:30	8:30	8:30
9:00	9:00	9:00
9:30	9:30	9:30
10:00	10:00	10:00
10:30	10:30	10:30
11:00	11:00	11:00

Ready for tomorrow?	( )	( )	( )
ALARM			
CLOTHES/BACKPACK			
GLASS OF WATER			
SAVERS PREP			
BEDTIME AFFIRMATIONS			

Wednesday	Thursday	Friday	Saturday
S	S	S	S
A	A	A	A
V	V	V	V
E	E	E	E
R	R	R	R
S	S	S	S
◆	◆	◆	◆
◆	◆	◆	◆

Wednesday	Thursday	Friday	Saturday
5:00	5:00	5:00	5:00
5:30	5:30	5:30	5:30
6:00	6:00	6:00	6:00
6:30	6:30	6:30	6:30
7:00	7:00	7:00	7:00
7:30	7:30	7:30	7:30
8:00	8:00	8:00	8:00
8:30	8:30	8:30	8:30
9:00	9:00	9:00	9:00
9:30	9:30	9:30	9:30
10:00	10:00	10:00	10:00
10:30	10:30	10:30	10:30
11:00	11:00	11:00	11:00
11:30	11:30	11:30	11:30
12:00	12:00	12:00	12:00
12:30	12:30	12:30	12:30
1:00	1:00	1:00	1:00
1:30	1:30	1:30	1:30
2:00	2:00	2:00	2:00
2:30	2:30	2:30	2:30
3:00	3:00	3:00	3:00
3:30	3:30	3:30	3:30
4:00	4:00	4:00	4:00
4:30	4:30	4:30	4:30
5:00	5:00	5:00	5:00
5:30	5:30	5:30	5:30
6:00	6:00	6:00	6:00
6:30	6:30	6:30	6:30
7:00	7:00	7:00	7:00
7:30	7:30	7:30	7:30
8:00	8:00	8:00	8:00
8:30	8:30	8:30	8:30
9:00	9:00	9:00	9:00
9:30	9:30	9:30	9:30
10:00	10:00	10:00	10:00
10:30	10:30	10:30	10:30
11:00	11:00	11:00	11:00

( )	( )	( )	( )

WEEKLY REFLECTION

· ·

1) What was my greatest accomplishment this week?

2) Who or what am I grateful for?

3) What activity from this last week took away from my focus and time?

4) What is one thing I can do to be better prepared for this week?

5) What am I looking forward to during the upcoming week?

BRAINSTORM

FINANCIAL CHECKBOX

Questions	Yes	No
Did I remain on budget this week?		
Did I buy what I needed over what I wanted?		
If you got paid this week, did you place 10% of it in your savings?		
Have I taken a percentage (1%-10%) to donate?		
Did I use my credit card wisely this week?		

How can I manage my money more wisely this week?

Week of:	Sunday		Monday		Tuesday	
This Week's Goal	S		S		S	
	A		A		A	
	V		V		V	
	E		E		E	
	R		R		R	
	S		S		S	
Intention for the Day	◆		◆		◆	
Grateful for ...	◆		◆		◆	

Either you run the day, or the day runs you.

—JIM ROHN

TO-DO LIST
Highest Priority

Definite Priority

Lowest Priority

Habit to Work on This Week

Sunday	Monday	Tuesday
5:00	5:00	5:00
5:30	5:30	5:30
6:00	6:00	6:00
6:30	6:30	6:30
7:00	7:00	7:00
7:30	7:30	7:30
8:00	8:00	8:00
8:30	8:30	8:30
9:00	9:00	9:00
9:30	9:30	9:30
10:00	10:00	10:00
10:30	10:30	10:30
11:00	11:00	11:00
11:30	11:30	11:30
12:00	12:00	12:00
12:30	12:30	12:30
1:00	1:00	1:00
1:30	1:30	1:30
2:00	2:00	2:00
2:30	2:30	2:30
3:00	3:00	3:00
3:30	3:30	3:30
4:00	4:00	4:00
4:30	4:30	4:30
5:00	5:00	5:00
5:30	5:30	5:30
6:00	6:00	6:00
6:30	6:30	6:30
7:00	7:00	7:00
7:30	7:30	7:30
8:00	8:00	8:00
8:30	8:30	8:30
9:00	9:00	9:00
9:30	9:30	9:30
10:00	10:00	10:00
10:30	10:30	10:30
11:00	11:00	11:00

Ready for tomorrow?	( )	( )	( )
ALARM			
CLOTHES/BACKPACK			
GLASS OF WATER			
SAVERS PREP			
BEDTIME AFFIRMATIONS			

Wednesday		Thursday		Friday		Saturday	
S		S		S		S	
A		A		A		A	
V		V		V		V	
E		E		E		E	
R		R		R		R	
S		S		S		S	
◆		◆		◆		◆	
◆		◆		◆		◆	
5:00		5:00		5:00		5:00	
5:30		5:30		5:30		5:30	
6:00		6:00		6:00		6:00	
6:30		6:30		6:30		6:30	
7:00		7:00		7:00		7:00	
7:30		7:30		7:30		7:30	
8:00		8:00		8:00		8:00	
8:30		8:30		8:30		8:30	
9:00		9:00		9:00		9:00	
9:30		9:30		9:30		9:30	
10:00		10:00		10:00		10:00	
10:30		10:30		10:30		10:30	
11:00		11:00		11:00		11:00	
11:30		11:30		11:30		11:30	
12:00		12:00		12:00		12:00	
12:30		12:30		12:30		12:30	
1:00		1:00		1:00		1:00	
1:30		1:30		1:30		1:30	
2:00		2:00		2:00		2:00	
2:30		2:30		2:30		2:30	
3:00		3:00		3:00		3:00	
3:30		3:30		3:30		3:30	
4:00		4:00		4:00		4:00	
4:30		4:30		4:30		4:30	
5:00		5:00		5:00		5:00	
5:30		5:30		5:30		5:30	
6:00		6:00		6:00		6:00	
6:30		6:30		6:30		6:30	
7:00		7:00		7:00		7:00	
7:30		7:30		7:30		7:30	
8:00		8:00		8:00		8:00	
8:30		8:30		8:30		8:30	
9:00		9:00		9:00		9:00	
9:30		9:30		9:30		9:30	
10:00		10:00		10:00		10:00	
10:30		10:30		10:30		10:30	
11:00		11:00		11:00		11:00	
	( )		( )		( )		( )

WEEKLY REFLECTION

....

1) What was my greatest accomplishment this week?

2) Who or what am I grateful for?

3) What activity from this last week took away from my focus and time?

4) What is one thing I can do to be better prepared for this week?

5) What am I looking forward to during the upcoming week?

BRAINSTORM

FINANCIAL CHECKBOX

Questions	Yes	No
Did I remain on budget this week?		
Did I buy what I needed over what I wanted?		
If you got paid this week, did you place 10% of it in your savings?		
Have I taken a percentage (1%-10%) to donate?		
Did I use my credit card wisely this week?		

How can I manage my money more wisely this week?

Week of:	Sunday	Monday	Tuesday
This Week's Goal	S	S	S
	A	A	A
	V	V	V
	E	E	E
	R	R	R
	S	S	S
Intention for the Day	◆	◆	◆
Grateful for ...	◆	◆	◆

Change your thoughts and you change your world.

—NORMAN VINCENT PEALE

TO-DO LIST
Highest Priority
Definite Priority
Lowest Priority
Habit to Work on This Week

Time	Sunday	Time	Monday	Time	Tuesday
5:00		5:00		5:00	
5:30		5:30		5:30	
6:00		6:00		6:00	
6:30		6:30		6:30	
7:00		7:00		7:00	
7:30		7:30		7:30	
8:00		8:00		8:00	
8:30		8:30		8:30	
9:00		9:00		9:00	
9:30		9:30		9:30	
10:00		10:00		10:00	
10:30		10:30		10:30	
11:00		11:00		11:00	
11:30		11:30		11:30	
12:00		12:00		12:00	
12:30		12:30		12:30	
1:00		1:00		1:00	
1:30		1:30		1:30	
2:00		2:00		2:00	
2:30		2:30		2:30	
3:00		3:00		3:00	
3:30		3:30		3:30	
4:00		4:00		4:00	
4:30		4:30		4:30	
5:00		5:00		5:00	
5:30		5:30		5:30	
6:00		6:00		6:00	
6:30		6:30		6:30	
7:00		7:00		7:00	
7:30		7:30		7:30	
8:00		8:00		8:00	
8:30		8:30		8:30	
9:00		9:00		9:00	
9:30		9:30		9:30	
10:00		10:00		10:00	
10:30		10:30		10:30	
11:00		11:00		11:00	

Ready for tomorrow?	( )	( )	( )
ALARM			
CLOTHES/BACKPACK			
GLASS OF WATER			
SAVERS PREP			
BEDTIME AFFIRMATIONS			

Wednesday	Thursday	Friday	Saturday
S	S	S	S
A	A	A	A
V	V	V	V
E	E	E	E
R	R	R	R
S	S	S	S

◆	◆	◆	◆
◆	◆	◆	◆

Wednesday	Thursday	Friday	Saturday
5:00	5:00	5:00	5:00
5:30	5:30	5:30	5:30
6:00	6:00	6:00	6:00
6:30	6:30	6:30	6:30
7:00	7:00	7:00	7:00
7:30	7:30	7:30	7:30
8:00	8:00	8:00	8:00
8:30	8:30	8:30	8:30
9:00	9:00	9:00	9:00
9:30	9:30	9:30	9:30
10:00	10:00	10:00	10:00
10:30	10:30	10:30	10:30
11:00	11:00	11:00	11:00
11:30	11:30	11:30	11:30
12:00	12:00	12:00	12:00
12:30	12:30	12:30	12:30
1:00	1:00	1:00	1:00
1:30	1:30	1:30	1:30
2:00	2:00	2:00	2:00
2:30	2:30	2:30	2:30
3:00	3:00	3:00	3:00
3:30	3:30	3:30	3:30
4:00	4:00	4:00	4:00
4:30	4:30	4:30	4:30
5:00	5:00	5:00	5:00
5:30	5:30	5:30	5:30
6:00	6:00	6:00	6:00
6:30	6:30	6:30	6:30
7:00	7:00	7:00	7:00
7:30	7:30	7:30	7:30
8:00	8:00	8:00	8:00
8:30	8:30	8:30	8:30
9:00	9:00	9:00	9:00
9:30	9:30	9:30	9:30
10:00	10:00	10:00	10:00
10:30	10:30	10:30	10:30
11:00	11:00	11:00	11:00

( )	( )	( )	( )

WEEKLY REFLECTION

•••

1) What was my greatest accomplishment this week?

2) Who or what am I grateful for?

3) What activity from this last week took away from my focus and time?

4) What is one thing I can do to be better prepared for this week?

5) What am I looking forward to during the upcoming week?

BRAINSTORM

FINANCIAL CHECKBOX

Questions	Yes	No
Did I remain on budget this week?		
Did I buy what I needed over what I wanted?		
If you got paid this week, did you place 10% of it in your savings?		
Have I taken a percentage (1%-10%) to donate?		
Did I use my credit card wisely this week?		
How can I manage my money more wisely this week?		

MONTHLY REFLECTION

Write 5 things you accomplished this month:

1.

2.

3.

4.

5.

QUESTIONS

1) What did I learn about myself this month?

2) What tasks are left over from this month that are lingering and need to get done?

3. Did I take care of myself?

4) What could I have done differently this past month?

5) What areas can I (still) improve on?

6) What experiences can I treasure?

7) What challenged me and how did I overcome the challenge?

8) What specific habits and/or rituals could I develop this month to support my vision?

MONTH OF:	SUNDAY	MONDAY	TUESDAY
This Month's Goal			
Important Events or Reminders to Transfer to My Phone			
1.			
2.			
3.			
4.			
5.			
6.			
7.			
8.			
9.			
10.			

PROJECT NAME	CLASS & INSTRUCTOR	IMPORTANT DATES	DEADLINES
1.			
2.			
3.			
4.			

WEDNESDAY	THURSDAY	FRIDAY	SATURDAY

BRAINSTORM

Week of:	Sunday	Monday	Tuesday
This Week's Goal	S	S	S
	A	A	A
	V	V	V
	E	E	E
	R	R	R
	S	S	S
Intention for the Day	◆	◆	◆
Grateful for ...	◆	◆	◆

Someday is not a day of the week.

—DENISE BRENNAN-NELSON

TO-DO LIST	Sunday	Monday	Tuesday
Highest Priority	5:00	5:00	5:00
	5:30	5:30	5:30
	6:00	6:00	6:00
	6:30	6:30	6:30
	7:00	7:00	7:00
	7:30	7:30	7:30
	8:00	8:00	8:00
	8:30	8:30	8:30
	9:00	9:00	9:00
	9:30	9:30	9:30
	10:00	10:00	10:00
	10:30	10:30	10:30
	11:00	11:00	11:00
	11:30	11:30	11:30
	12:00	12:00	12:00
	12:30	12:30	12:30
	1:00	1:00	1:00
Definite Priority	1:30	1:30	1:30
	2:00	2:00	2:00
	2:30	2:30	2:30
	3:00	3:00	3:00
	3:30	3:30	3:30
	4:00	4:00	4:00
Lowest Priority	4:30	4:30	4:30
	5:00	5:00	5:00
	5:30	5:30	5:30
	6:00	6:00	6:00
	6:30	6:30	6:30
	7:00	7:00	7:00
	7:30	7:30	7:30
Habit to Work on This Week	8:00	8:00	8:00
	8:30	8:30	8:30
	9:00	9:00	9:00
	9:30	9:30	9:30
	10:00	10:00	10:00
	10:30	10:30	10:30
	11:00	11:00	11:00

Ready for tomorrow?	( )	( )	( )
ALARM			
CLOTHES/BACKPACK			
GLASS OF WATER			
SAVERS PREP			
BEDTIME AFFIRMATIONS			

Wednesday	Thursday	Friday	Saturday
S	S	S	S
A	A	A	A
V	V	V	V
E	E	E	E
R	R	R	R
S	S	S	S

◆		◆		◆		◆	
◆		◆		◆		◆	

Wednesday		Thursday		Friday		Saturday	
5:00		5:00		5:00		5:00	
5:30		5:30		5:30		5:30	
6:00		6:00		6:00		6:00	
6:30		6:30		6:30		6:30	
7:00		7:00		7:00		7:00	
7:30		7:30		7:30		7:30	
8:00		8:00		8:00		8:00	
8:30		8:30		8:30		8:30	
9:00		9:00		9:00		9:00	
9:30		9:30		9:30		9:30	
10:00		10:00		10:00		10:00	
10:30		10:30		10:30		10:30	
11:00		11:00		11:00		11:00	
11:30		11:30		11:30		11:30	
12:00		12:00		12:00		12:00	
12:30		12:30		12:30		12:30	
1:00		1:00		1:00		1:00	
1:30		1:30		1:30		1:30	
2:00		2:00		2:00		2:00	
2:30		2:30		2:30		2:30	
3:00		3:00		3:00		3:00	
3:30		3:30		3:30		3:30	
4:00		4:00		4:00		4:00	
4:30		4:30		4:30		4:30	
5:00		5:00		5:00		5:00	
5:30		5:30		5:30		5:30	
6:00		6:00		6:00		6:00	
6:30		6:30		6:30		6:30	
7:00		7:00		7:00		7:00	
7:30		7:30		7:30		7:30	
8:00		8:00		8:00		8:00	
8:30		8:30		8:30		8:30	
9:00		9:00		9:00		9:00	
9:30		9:30		9:30		9:30	
10:00		10:00		10:00		10:00	
10:30		10:30		10:30		10:30	
11:00		11:00		11:00		11:00	

( )	( )	( )	( )

WEEKLY REFLECTION

. . . .

1) What was my greatest accomplishment this week?

2) Who or what am I grateful for?

3) What activity from this last week took away from my focus and time?

4) What is one thing I can do to be better prepared for this week?

5) What am I looking forward to during the upcoming week?

BRAINSTORM

FINANCIAL CHECKBOX

Questions	Yes	No
Did I remain on budget this week?		
Did I buy what I needed over what I wanted?		
If you got paid this week, did you place 10% of it in your savings?		
Have I taken a percentage (1%-10%) to donate?		
Did I use my credit card wisely this week?		
How can I manage my money more wisely this week?		

Week of:	Sunday	Monday	Tuesday
This Week's Goal	S	S	S
	A	A	A
	V	V	V
	E	E	E
	R	R	R
	S	S	S
Intention for the Day	◆	◆	◆
Grateful for ...	◆	◆	◆

The journey of a thousand miles begins with one step.

—LAO TZU

TO-DO LIST

Highest Priority

Definite Priority

Lowest Priority

Habit to Work on This Week

Time	Sunday	Monday	Tuesday
5:00			
5:30			
6:00			
6:30			
7:00			
7:30			
8:00			
8:30			
9:00			
9:30			
10:00			
10:30			
11:00			
11:30			
12:00			
12:30			
1:00			
1:30			
2:00			
2:30			
3:00			
3:30			
4:00			
4:30			
5:00			
5:30			
6:00			
6:30			
7:00			
7:30			
8:00			
8:30			
9:00			
9:30			
10:00			
10:30			
11:00			

Ready for tomorrow?	( )	( )	( )
ALARM			
CLOTHES/BACKPACK			
GLASS OF WATER			
SAVERS PREP			
BEDTIME AFFIRMATIONS			

Wednesday		Thursday		Friday		Saturday	
S		S		S		S	
A		A		A		A	
V		V		V		V	
E		E		E		E	
R		R		R		R	
S		S		S		S	

◆		◆		◆		◆	
◆		◆		◆		◆	

Wednesday	Thursday	Friday	Saturday
5:00	5:00	5:00	5:00
5:30	5:30	5:30	5:30
6:00	6:00	6:00	6:00
6:30	6:30	6:30	6:30
7:00	7:00	7:00	7:00
7:30	7:30	7:30	7:30
8:00	8:00	8:00	8:00
8:30	8:30	8:30	8:30
9:00	9:00	9:00	9:00
9:30	9:30	9:30	9:30
10:00	10:00	10:00	10:00
10:30	10:30	10:30	10:30
11:00	11:00	11:00	11:00
11:30	11:30	11:30	11:30
12:00	12:00	12:00	12:00
12:30	12:30	12:30	12:30
1:00	1:00	1:00	1:00
1:30	1:30	1:30	1:30
2:00	2:00	2:00	2:00
2:30	2:30	2:30	2:30
3:00	3:00	3:00	3:00
3:30	3:30	3:30	3:30
4:00	4:00	4:00	4:00
4:30	4:30	4:30	4:30
5:00	5:00	5:00	5:00
5:30	5:30	5:30	5:30
6:00	6:00	6:00	6:00
6:30	6:30	6:30	6:30
7:00	7:00	7:00	7:00
7:30	7:30	7:30	7:30
8:00	8:00	8:00	8:00
8:30	8:30	8:30	8:30
9:00	9:00	9:00	9:00
9:30	9:30	9:30	9:30
10:00	10:00	10:00	10:00
10:30	10:30	10:30	10:30
11:00	11:00	11:00	11:00

( )	( )	( )	( )

WEEKLY REFLECTION

....

1) What was my greatest accomplishment this week?

2) Who or what am I grateful for?

3) What activity from this last week took away from my focus and time?

4) What is one thing I can do to be better prepared for this week?

5) What am I looking forward to during the upcoming week?

BRAINSTORM

FINANCIAL CHECKBOX

Questions	Yes	No
Did I remain on budget this week?		
Did I buy what I needed over what I wanted?		
If you got paid this week, did you place 10% of it in your savings?		
Have I taken a percentage (1%-10%) to donate?		
Did I use my credit card wisely this week?		
How can I manage my money more wisely this week?		

Week of:	Sunday	Monday	Tuesday
This Week's Goal	S	S	S
	A	A	A
	V	V	V
	E	E	E
	R	R	R
	S	S	S
Intention for the Day	◆	◆	◆
Grateful for ...	◆	◆	◆

Kindness is the language which the deaf can hear and the blind can see.

—MARK TWAIN

TO-DO LIST

Highest Priority

Definite Priority

Lowest Priority

Habit to Work on This Week

Sunday	Monday	Tuesday
5:00	5:00	5:00
5:30	5:30	5:30
6:00	6:00	6:00
6:30	6:30	6:30
7:00	7:00	7:00
7:30	7:30	7:30
8:00	8:00	8:00
8:30	8:30	8:30
9:00	9:00	9:00
9:30	9:30	9:30
10:00	10:00	10:00
10:30	10:30	10:30
11:00	11:00	11:00
11:30	11:30	11:30
12:00	12:00	12:00
12:30	12:30	12:30
1:00	1:00	1:00
1:30	1:30	1:30
2:00	2:00	2:00
2:30	2:30	2:30
3:00	3:00	3:00
3:30	3:30	3:30
4:00	4:00	4:00
4:30	4:30	4:30
5:00	5:00	5:00
5:30	5:30	5:30
6:00	6:00	6:00
6:30	6:30	6:30
7:00	7:00	7:00
7:30	7:30	7:30
8:00	8:00	8:00
8:30	8:30	8:30
9:00	9:00	9:00
9:30	9:30	9:30
10:00	10:00	10:00
10:30	10:30	10:30
11:00	11:00	11:00

Ready for tomorrow?	( )	( )	( )
ALARM			
CLOTHES/BACKPACK			
GLASS OF WATER			
SAVERS PREP			
BEDTIME AFFIRMATIONS			

Wednesday	Thursday	Friday	Saturday
S	S	S	S
A	A	A	A
V	V	V	V
E	E	E	E
R	R	R	R
S	S	S	S
◆	◆	◆	◆
◆	◆	◆	◆

Wednesday	Thursday	Friday	Saturday
5:00	5:00	5:00	5:00
5:30	5:30	5:30	5:30
6:00	6:00	6:00	6:00
6:30	6:30	6:30	6:30
7:00	7:00	7:00	7:00
7:30	7:30	7:30	7:30
8:00	8:00	8:00	8:00
8:30	8:30	8:30	8:30
9:00	9:00	9:00	9:00
9:30	9:30	9:30	9:30
10:00	10:00	10:00	10:00
10:30	10:30	10:30	10:30
11:00	11:00	11:00	11:00
11:30	11:30	11:30	11:30
12:00	12:00	12:00	12:00
12:30	12:30	12:30	12:30
1:00	1:00	1:00	1:00
1:30	1:30	1:30	1:30
2:00	2:00	2:00	2:00
2:30	2:30	2:30	2:30
3:00	3:00	3:00	3:00
3:30	3:30	3:30	3:30
4:00	4:00	4:00	4:00
4:30	4:30	4:30	4:30
5:00	5:00	5:00	5:00
5:30	5:30	5:30	5:30
6:00	6:00	6:00	6:00
6:30	6:30	6:30	6:30
7:00	7:00	7:00	7:00
7:30	7:30	7:30	7:30
8:00	8:00	8:00	8:00
8:30	8:30	8:30	8:30
9:00	9:00	9:00	9:00
9:30	9:30	9:30	9:30
10:00	10:00	10:00	10:00
10:30	10:30	10:30	10:30
11:00	11:00	11:00	11:00

( )	( )	( )	( )

WEEKLY REFLECTION

. . . .

1) What was my greatest accomplishment this week?

2) Who or what am I grateful for?

3) What activity from this last week took away from my focus and time?

4) What is one thing I can do to be better prepared for this week?

5) What am I looking forward to during the upcoming week?

BRAINSTORM

FINANCIAL CHECKBOX

Questions	Yes	No
Did I remain on budget this week?		
Did I buy what I needed over what I wanted?		
If you got paid this week, did you place 10% of it in your savings?		
Have I taken a percentage (1%-10%) to donate?		
Did I use my credit card wisely this week?		

How can I manage my money more wisely this week?

Week of:	Sunday	Monday	Tuesday
This Week's Goal	S	S	S
	A	A	A
	V	V	V
	E	E	E
	R	R	R
	S	S	S
Intention for the Day	◆	◆	◆
Grateful for ...	◆	◆	◆

The body heals with play, the mind heals with laughter, and the spirit heals with joy.

—PROVERB

TO-DO LIST

Highest Priority

Definite Priority

Lowest Priority

Habit to Work on This Week

Time	Sunday	Time	Monday	Time	Tuesday
5:00		5:00		5:00	
5:30		5:30		5:30	
6:00		6:00		6:00	
6:30		6:30		6:30	
7:00		7:00		7:00	
7:30		7:30		7:30	
8:00		8:00		8:00	
8:30		8:30		8:30	
9:00		9:00		9:00	
9:30		9:30		9:30	
10:00		10:00		10:00	
10:30		10:30		10:30	
11:00		11:00		11:00	
11:30		11:30		11:30	
12:00		12:00		12:00	
12:30		12:30		12:30	
1:00		1:00		1:00	
1:30		1:30		1:30	
2:00		2:00		2:00	
2:30		2:30		2:30	
3:00		3:00		3:00	
3:30		3:30		3:30	
4:00		4:00		4:00	
4:30		4:30		4:30	
5:00		5:00		5:00	
5:30		5:30		5:30	
6:00		6:00		6:00	
6:30		6:30		6:30	
7:00		7:00		7:00	
7:30		7:30		7:30	
8:00		8:00		8:00	
8:30		8:30		8:30	
9:00		9:00		9:00	
9:30		9:30		9:30	
10:00		10:00		10:00	
10:30		10:30		10:30	
11:00		11:00		11:00	

Ready for tomorrow?	( )	( )	( )
ALARM			
CLOTHES/BACKPACK			
GLASS OF WATER			
SAVERS PREP			
BEDTIME AFFIRMATIONS			

Wednesday	Thursday	Friday	Saturday
S	S	S	S
A	A	A	A
V	V	V	V
E	E	E	E
R	R	R	R
S	S	S	S

◆	◆	◆	◆
◆	◆	◆	◆

Time	Wednesday	Time	Thursday	Time	Friday	Time	Saturday
5:00		5:00		5:00		5:00	
5:30		5:30		5:30		5:30	
6:00		6:00		6:00		6:00	
6:30		6:30		6:30		6:30	
7:00		7:00		7:00		7:00	
7:30		7:30		7:30		7:30	
8:00		8:00		8:00		8:00	
8:30		8:30		8:30		8:30	
9:00		9:00		9:00		9:00	
9:30		9:30		9:30		9:30	
10:00		10:00		10:00		10:00	
10:30		10:30		10:30		10:30	
11:00		11:00		11:00		11:00	
11:30		11:30		11:30		11:30	
12:00		12:00		12:00		12:00	
12:30		12:30		12:30		12:30	
1:00		1:00		1:00		1:00	
1:30		1:30		1:30		1:30	
2:00		2:00		2:00		2:00	
2:30		2:30		2:30		2:30	
3:00		3:00		3:00		3:00	
3:30		3:30		3:30		3:30	
4:00		4:00		4:00		4:00	
4:30		4:30		4:30		4:30	
5:00		5:00		5:00		5:00	
5:30		5:30		5:30		5:30	
6:00		6:00		6:00		6:00	
6:30		6:30		6:30		6:30	
7:00		7:00		7:00		7:00	
7:30		7:30		7:30		7:30	
8:00		8:00		8:00		8:00	
8:30		8:30		8:30		8:30	
9:00		9:00		9:00		9:00	
9:30		9:30		9:30		9:30	
10:00		10:00		10:00		10:00	
10:30		10:30		10:30		10:30	
11:00		11:00		11:00		11:00	

( )	( )	( )	( )

WEEKLY REFLECTION

• •

1) What was my greatest accomplishment this week?

2) Who or what am I grateful for?

3) What activity from this last week took away from my focus and time?

4) What is one thing I can do to be better prepared for this week?

5) What am I looking forward to during the upcoming week?

BRAINSTORM

FINANCIAL CHECKBOX

Questions	Yes	No
Did I remain on budget this week?		
Did I buy what I needed over what I wanted?		
If you got paid this week, did you place 10% of it in your savings?		
Have I taken a percentage (1%-10%) to donate?		
Did I use my credit card wisely this week?		

How can I manage my money more wisely this week?

Week of:	Sunday	Monday	Tuesday
This Week's Goal	S	S	S
	A	A	A
	V	V	V
	E	E	E
	R	R	R
	S	S	S
Intention for the Day	◆	◆	◆
Grateful for ...	◆	◆	◆

There are only two ways to live your life. One is as though nothing is a miracle. The other is as though everything is a miracle.

—ALBERT EINSTEIN

TO-DO LIST

Highest Priority

Definite Priority

Lowest Priority

Habit to Work on This Week

Sunday	Monday	Tuesday
5:00	5:00	5:00
5:30	5:30	5:30
6:00	6:00	6:00
6:30	6:30	6:30
7:00	7:00	7:00
7:30	7:30	7:30
8:00	8:00	8:00
8:30	8:30	8:30
9:00	9:00	9:00
9:30	9:30	9:30
10:00	10:00	10:00
10:30	10:30	10:30
11:00	11:00	11:00
11:30	11:30	11:30
12:00	12:00	12:00
12:30	12:30	12:30
1:00	1:00	1:00
1:30	1:30	1:30
2:00	2:00	2:00
2:30	2:30	2:30
3:00	3:00	3:00
3:30	3:30	3:30
4:00	4:00	4:00
4:30	4:30	4:30
5:00	5:00	5:00
5:30	5:30	5:30
6:00	6:00	6:00
6:30	6:30	6:30
7:00	7:00	7:00
7:30	7:30	7:30
8:00	8:00	8:00
8:30	8:30	8:30
9:00	9:00	9:00
9:30	9:30	9:30
10:00	10:00	10:00
10:30	10:30	10:30
11:00	11:00	11:00

Ready for tomorrow?	( )	( )	( )
ALARM			
CLOTHES/BACKPACK			
GLASS OF WATER			
SAVERS PREP			
BEDTIME AFFIRMATIONS			

Wednesday	Thursday	Friday	Saturday
S	S	S	S
A	A	A	A
V	V	V	V
E	E	E	E
R	R	R	R
S	S	S	S
◆	◆	◆	◆
◆	◆	◆	◆

Wednesday	Thursday	Friday	Saturday
5:00	5:00	5:00	5:00
5:30	5:30	5:30	5:30
6:00	6:00	6:00	6:00
6:30	6:30	6:30	6:30
7:00	7:00	7:00	7:00
7:30	7:30	7:30	7:30
8:00	8:00	8:00	8:00
8:30	8:30	8:30	8:30
9:00	9:00	9:00	9:00
9:30	9:30	9:30	9:30
10:00	10:00	10:00	10:00
10:30	10:30	10:30	10:30
11:00	11:00	11:00	11:00
11:30	11:30	11:30	11:30
12:00	12:00	12:00	12:00
12:30	12:30	12:30	12:30
1:00	1:00	1:00	1:00
1:30	1:30	1:30	1:30
2:00	2:00	2:00	2:00
2:30	2:30	2:30	2:30
3:00	3:00	3:00	3:00
3:30	3:30	3:30	3:30
4:00	4:00	4:00	4:00
4:30	4:30	4:30	4:30
5:00	5:00	5:00	5:00
5:30	5:30	5:30	5:30
6:00	6:00	6:00	6:00
6:30	6:30	6:30	6:30
7:00	7:00	7:00	7:00
7:30	7:30	7:30	7:30
8:00	8:00	8:00	8:00
8:30	8:30	8:30	8:30
9:00	9:00	9:00	9:00
9:30	9:30	9:30	9:30
10:00	10:00	10:00	10:00
10:30	10:30	10:30	10:30
11:00	11:00	11:00	11:00
( )	( )	( )	( )

WEEKLY REFLECTION

. . . .

1) What was my greatest accomplishment this week?

2) Who or what am I grateful for?

3) What activity from this last week took away from my focus and time?

4) What is one thing I can do to be better prepared for this week?

5) What am I looking forward to during the upcoming week?

BRAINSTORM

FINANCIAL CHECKBOX

Questions	Yes	No
Did I remain on budget this week?		
Did I buy what I needed over what I wanted?		
If you got paid this week, did you place 10% of it in your savings?		
Have I taken a percentage (1%-10%) to donate?		
Did I use my credit card wisely this week?		

How can I manage my money more wisely this week?

MONTHLY REFLECTION

· ·

Write 5 things you accomplished this month:

1.

2.

3.

4.

5.

QUESTIONS

1) What did I learn about myself this month?

2) What tasks are left over from this month that are lingering and need to get done?

3. Did I take care of myself?

4) What could I have done differently this past month?

5) What areas can I (still) improve on?

6) What experiences can I treasure?

7) What challenged me and how did I overcome the challenge?

8) What specific habits and/or rituals could I develop this month to support my vision?

MONTH OF:	SUNDAY	MONDAY	TUESDAY
This Month's Goal			
Important Events or Reminders to Transfer to My Phone			
1.			
2.			
3.			
4.			
5.			
6.			
7.			
8.			
9.			
10.			

PROJECT NAME	CLASS & INSTRUCTOR	IMPORTANT DATES	DEADLINES
1.			
2.			
3.			
4.			

WEDNESDAY	THURSDAY	FRIDAY	SATURDAY

BRAINSTORM

Week of:		Sunday		Monday		Tuesday	
This Week's Goal		S		S		S	
		A		A		A	
		V		V		V	
		E		E		E	
		R		R		R	
		S		S		S	
Intention for the Day		◆		◆		◆	
Grateful for …		◆		◆		◆	

An extraordinary life is all about daily, continuous improvements in the areas that matter most.

—ROBIN SHARMA

TO-DO LIST	Sunday	Monday	Tuesday
Highest Priority	5:00	5:00	5:00
	5:30	5:30	5:30
	6:00	6:00	6:00
	6:30	6:30	6:30
	7:00	7:00	7:00
	7:30	7:30	7:30
	8:00	8:00	8:00
	8:30	8:30	8:30
	9:00	9:00	9:00
	9:30	9:30	9:30
	10:00	10:00	10:00
	10:30	10:30	10:30
	11:00	11:00	11:00
	11:30	11:30	11:30
	12:00	12:00	12:00
	12:30	12:30	12:30
	1:00	1:00	1:00
Definite Priority	1:30	1:30	1:30
	2:00	2:00	2:00
	2:30	2:30	2:30
	3:00	3:00	3:00
	3:30	3:30	3:30
	4:00	4:00	4:00
Lowest Priority	4:30	4:30	4:30
	5:00	5:00	5:00
	5:30	5:30	5:30
	6:00	6:00	6:00
	6:30	6:30	6:30
	7:00	7:00	7:00
	7:30	7:30	7:30
Habit to Work on This Week	8:00	8:00	8:00
	8:30	8:30	8:30
	9:00	9:00	9:00
	9:30	9:30	9:30
	10:00	10:00	10:00
	10:30	10:30	10:30
	11:00	11:00	11:00

Ready for tomorrow?	( )	( )	( )
ALARM			
CLOTHES/BACKPACK			
GLASS OF WATER			
SAVERS PREP			
BEDTIME AFFIRMATIONS			

Wednesday	Thursday	Friday	Saturday
S	S	S	S
A	A	A	A
V	V	V	V
E	E	E	E
R	R	R	R
S	S	S	S
◆	◆	◆	◆
◆	◆	◆	◆

	Wednesday		Thursday		Friday		Saturday
5:00		5:00		5:00		5:00	
5:30		5:30		5:30		5:30	
6:00		6:00		6:00		6:00	
6:30		6:30		6:30		6:30	
7:00		7:00		7:00		7:00	
7:30		7:30		7:30		7:30	
8:00		8:00		8:00		8:00	
8:30		8:30		8:30		8:30	
9:00		9:00		9:00		9:00	
9:30		9:30		9:30		9:30	
10:00		10:00		10:00		10:00	
10:30		10:30		10:30		10:30	
11:00		11:00		11:00		11:00	
11:30		11:30		11:30		11:30	
12:00		12:00		12:00		12:00	
12:30		12:30		12:30		12:30	
1:00		1:00		1:00		1:00	
1:30		1:30		1:30		1:30	
2:00		2:00		2:00		2:00	
2:30		2:30		2:30		2:30	
3:00		3:00		3:00		3:00	
3:30		3:30		3:30		3:30	
4:00		4:00		4:00		4:00	
4:30		4:30		4:30		4:30	
5:00		5:00		5:00		5:00	
5:30		5:30		5:30		5:30	
6:00		6:00		6:00		6:00	
6:30		6:30		6:30		6:30	
7:00		7:00		7:00		7:00	
7:30		7:30		7:30		7:30	
8:00		8:00		8:00		8:00	
8:30		8:30		8:30		8:30	
9:00		9:00		9:00		9:00	
9:30		9:30		9:30		9:30	
10:00		10:00		10:00		10:00	
10:30		10:30		10:30		10:30	
11:00		11:00		11:00		11:00	

	( )		( )		( )		( )

WEEKLY REFLECTION

....

1) What was my greatest accomplishment this week?

2) Who or what am I grateful for?

3) What activity from this last week took away from my focus and time?

4) What is one thing I can do to be better prepared for this week?

5) What am I looking forward to during the upcoming week?

BRAINSTORM

FINANCIAL CHECKBOX

Questions	Yes	No
Did I remain on budget this week?		
Did I buy what I needed over what I wanted?		
If you got paid this week, did you place 10% of it in your savings?		
Have I taken a percentage (1%-10%) to donate?		
Did I use my credit card wisely this week?		
How can I manage my money more wisely this week?		

Week of:	Sunday		Monday		Tuesday	
This Week's Goal	S		S		S	
	A		A		A	
	V		V		V	
	E		E		E	
	R		R		R	
	S		S		S	
Intention for the Day	◆		◆		◆	
Grateful for …	◆		◆		◆	

> *Whether you think you can or you think you can't, you're right.*
>
> **—HENRY FORD**

TO-DO LIST		Sunday		Monday		Tuesday
Highest Priority	5:00		5:00		5:00	
	5:30		5:30		5:30	
	6:00		6:00		6:00	
	6:30		6:30		6:30	
	7:00		7:00		7:00	
	7:30		7:30		7:30	
	8:00		8:00		8:00	
	8:30		8:30		8:30	
	9:00		9:00		9:00	
	9:30		9:30		9:30	
	10:00		10:00		10:00	
	10:30		10:30		10:30	
	11:00		11:00		11:00	
	11:30		11:30		11:30	
	12:00		12:00		12:00	
	12:30		12:30		12:30	
	1:00		1:00		1:00	
Definite Priority	1:30		1:30		1:30	
	2:00		2:00		2:00	
	2:30		2:30		2:30	
	3:00		3:00		3:00	
	3:30		3:30		3:30	
	4:00		4:00		4:00	
Lowest Priority	4:30		4:30		4:30	
	5:00		5:00		5:00	
	5:30		5:30		5:30	
	6:00		6:00		6:00	
	6:30		6:30		6:30	
	7:00		7:00		7:00	
	7:30		7:30		7:30	
Habit to Work on This Week	8:00		8:00		8:00	
	8:30		8:30		8:30	
	9:00		9:00		9:00	
	9:30		9:30		9:30	
	10:00		10:00		10:00	
	10:30		10:30		10:30	
	11:00		11:00		11:00	

Ready for tomorrow?	( )	( )	( )
ALARM			
CLOTHES/BACKPACK			
GLASS OF WATER			
SAVERS PREP			
BEDTIME AFFIRMATIONS			

Wednesday	Thursday	Friday	Saturday
S	S	S	S
A	A	A	A
V	V	V	V
E	E	E	E
R	R	R	R
S	S	S	S

◆	◆	◆	◆
◆	◆	◆	◆

Wednesday	Thursday	Friday	Saturday
5:00	5:00	5:00	5:00
5:30	5:30	5:30	5:30
6:00	6:00	6:00	6:00
6:30	6:30	6:30	6:30
7:00	7:00	7:00	7:00
7:30	7:30	7:30	7:30
8:00	8:00	8:00	8:00
8:30	8:30	8:30	8:30
9:00	9:00	9:00	9:00
9:30	9:30	9:30	9:30
10:00	10:00	10:00	10:00
10:30	10:30	10:30	10:30
11:00	11:00	11:00	11:00
11:30	11:30	11:30	11:30
12:00	12:00	12:00	12:00
12:30	12:30	12:30	12:30
1:00	1:00	1:00	1:00
1:30	1:30	1:30	1:30
2:00	2:00	2:00	2:00
2:30	2:30	2:30	2:30
3:00	3:00	3:00	3:00
3:30	3:30	3:30	3:30
4:00	4:00	4:00	4:00
4:30	4:30	4:30	4:30
5:00	5:00	5:00	5:00
5:30	5:30	5:30	5:30
6:00	6:00	6:00	6:00
6:30	6:30	6:30	6:30
7:00	7:00	7:00	7:00
7:30	7:30	7:30	7:30
8:00	8:00	8:00	8:00
8:30	8:30	8:30	8:30
9:00	9:00	9:00	9:00
9:30	9:30	9:30	9:30
10:00	10:00	10:00	10:00
10:30	10:30	10:30	10:30
11:00	11:00	11:00	11:00

( )	( )	( )	( )

WEEKLY REFLECTION

• •

1) What was my greatest accomplishment this week?

2) Who or what am I grateful for?

3) What activity from this last week took away from my focus and time?

4) What is one thing I can do to be better prepared for this week?

5) What am I looking forward to during the upcoming week?

BRAINSTORM

FINANCIAL CHECKBOX

Questions	Yes	No
Did I remain on budget this week?		
Did I buy what I needed over what I wanted?		
If you got paid this week, did you place 10% of it in your savings?		
Have I taken a percentage (1%-10%) to donate?		
Did I use my credit card wisely this week?		

How can I manage my money more wisely this week?

Week of:	Sunday		Monday		Tuesday	
This Week's Goal	S		S		S	
	A		A		A	
	V		V		V	
	E		E		E	
	R		R		R	
	S		S		S	
Intention for the Day	◆		◆		◆	
Grateful for ...	◆		◆		◆	

You miss 100% of the shots you don't take.

—WAYNE GRETZKY

TO-DO LIST	Sunday	Monday	Tuesday
Highest Priority	5:00	5:00	5:00
	5:30	5:30	5:30
	6:00	6:00	6:00
	6:30	6:30	6:30
	7:00	7:00	7:00
	7:30	7:30	7:30
	8:00	8:00	8:00
	8:30	8:30	8:30
	9:00	9:00	9:00
	9:30	9:30	9:30
	10:00	10:00	10:00
	10:30	10:30	10:30
	11:00	11:00	11:00
	11:30	11:30	11:30
	12:00	12:00	12:00
	12:30	12:30	12:30
	1:00	1:00	1:00
Definite Priority	1:30	1:30	1:30
	2:00	2:00	2:00
	2:30	2:30	2:30
	3:00	3:00	3:00
	3:30	3:30	3:30
	4:00	4:00	4:00
Lowest Priority	4:30	4:30	4:30
	5:00	5:00	5:00
	5:30	5:30	5:30
	6:00	6:00	6:00
	6:30	6:30	6:30
	7:00	7:00	7:00
	7:30	7:30	7:30
Habit to Work on This Week	8:00	8:00	8:00
	8:30	8:30	8:30
	9:00	9:00	9:00
	9:30	9:30	9:30
	10:00	10:00	10:00
	10:30	10:30	10:30
	11:00	11:00	11:00

Ready for tomorrow?	( )	( )	( )
ALARM			
CLOTHES/BACKPACK			
GLASS OF WATER			
SAVERS PREP			
BEDTIME AFFIRMATIONS			

Wednesday		Thursday		Friday		Saturday	
S		S		S		S	
A		A		A		A	
V		V		V		V	
E		E		E		E	
R		R		R		R	
S		S		S		S	
◆		◆		◆		◆	
◆		◆		◆		◆	

Wednesday		Thursday		Friday		Saturday	
5:00		5:00		5:00		5:00	
5:30		5:30		5:30		5:30	
6:00		6:00		6:00		6:00	
6:30		6:30		6:30		6:30	
7:00		7:00		7:00		7:00	
7:30		7:30		7:30		7:30	
8:00		8:00		8:00		8:00	
8:30		8:30		8:30		8:30	
9:00		9:00		9:00		9:00	
9:30		9:30		9:30		9:30	
10:00		10:00		10:00		10:00	
10:30		10:30		10:30		10:30	
11:00		11:00		11:00		11:00	
11:30		11:30		11:30		11:30	
12:00		12:00		12:00		12:00	
12:30		12:30		12:30		12:30	
1:00		1:00		1:00		1:00	
1:30		1:30		1:30		1:30	
2:00		2:00		2:00		2:00	
2:30		2:30		2:30		2:30	
3:00		3:00		3:00		3:00	
3:30		3:30		3:30		3:30	
4:00		4:00		4:00		4:00	
4:30		4:30		4:30		4:30	
5:00		5:00		5:00		5:00	
5:30		5:30		5:30		5:30	
6:00		6:00		6:00		6:00	
6:30		6:30		6:30		6:30	
7:00		7:00		7:00		7:00	
7:30		7:30		7:30		7:30	
8:00		8:00		8:00		8:00	
8:30		8:30		8:30		8:30	
9:00		9:00		9:00		9:00	
9:30		9:30		9:30		9:30	
10:00		10:00		10:00		10:00	
10:30		10:30		10:30		10:30	
11:00		11:00		11:00		11:00	
	( )		( )		( )		( )

WEEKLY REFLECTION

• •

1) What was my greatest accomplishment this week?

2) Who or what am I grateful for?

3) What activity from this last week took away from my focus and time?

4) What is one thing I can do to be better prepared for this week?

5) What am I looking forward to during the upcoming week?

BRAINSTORM

FINANCIAL CHECKBOX

Questions	Yes	No
Did I remain on budget this week?		
Did I buy what I needed over what I wanted?		
If you got paid this week, did you place 10% of it in your savings?		
Have I taken a percentage (1%-10%) to donate?		
Did I use my credit card wisely this week?		

How can I manage my money more wisely this week?

Week of:		Sunday		Monday		Tuesday
This Week's Goal		S		S		S
		A		A		A
		V		V		V
		E		E		E
		R		R		R
		S		S		S
Intention for the Day		◆		◆		◆
Grateful for …		◆		◆		◆

	Sunday		Monday		Tuesday
Success is going from failure to failure without losing your enthusiasm. —WINSTON CHURCHILL	5:00		5:00		5:00
	5:30		5:30		5:30
	6:00		6:00		6:00
	6:30		6:30		6:30
	7:00		7:00		7:00
	7:30		7:30		7:30
	8:00		8:00		8:00
	8:30		8:30		8:30
	9:00		9:00		9:00
	9:30		9:30		9:30
TO-DO LIST	10:00		10:00		10:00
Highest Priority	10:30		10:30		10:30
	11:00		11:00		11:00
	11:30		11:30		11:30
	12:00		12:00		12:00
	12:30		12:30		12:30
	1:00		1:00		1:00
Definite Priority	1:30		1:30		1:30
	2:00		2:00		2:00
	2:30		2:30		2:30
	3:00		3:00		3:00
	3:30		3:30		3:30
	4:00		4:00		4:00
Lowest Priority	4:30		4:30		4:30
	5:00		5:00		5:00
	5:30		5:30		5:30
	6:00		6:00		6:00
	6:30		6:30		6:30
	7:00		7:00		7:00
	7:30		7:30		7:30
Habit to Work on This Week	8:00		8:00		8:00
	8:30		8:30		8:30
	9:00		9:00		9:00
	9:30		9:30		9:30
	10:00		10:00		10:00
	10:30		10:30		10:30
	11:00		11:00		11:00

Ready for tomorrow?		( )		( )		( )
ALARM						
CLOTHES/BACKPACK						
GLASS OF WATER						
SAVERS PREP						
BEDTIME AFFIRMATIONS						

Wednesday		Thursday		Friday		Saturday	
S		S		S		S	
A		A		A		A	
V		V		V		V	
E		E		E		E	
R		R		R		R	
S		S		S		S	

◆		◆		◆		◆	
◆		◆		◆		◆	

Wednesday	Thursday	Friday	Saturday
5:00	5:00	5:00	5:00
5:30	5:30	5:30	5:30
6:00	6:00	6:00	6:00
6:30	6:30	6:30	6:30
7:00	7:00	7:00	7:00
7:30	7:30	7:30	7:30
8:00	8:00	8:00	8:00
8:30	8:30	8:30	8:30
9:00	9:00	9:00	9:00
9:30	9:30	9:30	9:30
10:00	10:00	10:00	10:00
10:30	10:30	10:30	10:30
11:00	11:00	11:00	11:00
11:30	11:30	11:30	11:30
12:00	12:00	12:00	12:00
12:30	12:30	12:30	12:30
1:00	1:00	1:00	1:00
1:30	1:30	1:30	1:30
2:00	2:00	2:00	2:00
2:30	2:30	2:30	2:30
3:00	3:00	3:00	3:00
3:30	3:30	3:30	3:30
4:00	4:00	4:00	4:00
4:30	4:30	4:30	4:30
5:00	5:00	5:00	5:00
5:30	5:30	5:30	5:30
6:00	6:00	6:00	6:00
6:30	6:30	6:30	6:30
7:00	7:00	7:00	7:00
7:30	7:30	7:30	7:30
8:00	8:00	8:00	8:00
8:30	8:30	8:30	8:30
9:00	9:00	9:00	9:00
9:30	9:30	9:30	9:30
10:00	10:00	10:00	10:00
10:30	10:30	10:30	10:30
11:00	11:00	11:00	11:00

( )	( )	( )	( )

WEEKLY REFLECTION

· ·

1) What was my greatest accomplishment this week?

2) Who or what am I grateful for?

3) What activity from this last week took away from my focus and time?

4) What is one thing I can do to be better prepared for this week?

5) What am I looking forward to during the upcoming week?

BRAINSTORM

FINANCIAL CHECKBOX

Questions	Yes	No
Did I remain on budget this week?		
Did I buy what I needed over what I wanted?		
If you got paid this week, did you place 10% of it in your savings?		
Have I taken a percentage (1%-10%) to donate?		
Did I use my credit card wisely this week?		
How can I manage my money more wisely this week?		

Week of:	Sunday	Monday	Tuesday
This Week's Goal	S	S	S
	A	A	A
	V	V	V
	E	E	E
	R	R	R
	S	S	S
Intention for the Day	◆	◆	◆
Grateful for ...	◆	◆	◆

Whatever you can do, or dream you can, begin it. Boldness has genius, power and magic in it.

–JOHANN WOLFGANG VON GOETHE

TO-DO LIST
Highest Priority
Definite Priority
Lowest Priority
Habit to Work on This Week

Sunday	Monday	Tuesday
5:00	5:00	5:00
5:30	5:30	5:30
6:00	6:00	6:00
6:30	6:30	6:30
7:00	7:00	7:00
7:30	7:30	7:30
8:00	8:00	8:00
8:30	8:30	8:30
9:00	9:00	9:00
9:30	9:30	9:30
10:00	10:00	10:00
10:30	10:30	10:30
11:00	11:00	11:00
11:30	11:30	11:30
12:00	12:00	12:00
12:30	12:30	12:30
1:00	1:00	1:00
1:30	1:30	1:30
2:00	2:00	2:00
2:30	2:30	2:30
3:00	3:00	3:00
3:30	3:30	3:30
4:00	4:00	4:00
4:30	4:30	4:30
5:00	5:00	5:00
5:30	5:30	5:30
6:00	6:00	6:00
6:30	6:30	6:30
7:00	7:00	7:00
7:30	7:30	7:30
8:00	8:00	8:00
8:30	8:30	8:30
9:00	9:00	9:00
9:30	9:30	9:30
10:00	10:00	10:00
10:30	10:30	10:30
11:00	11:00	11:00

Ready for tomorrow?	( )	( )	( )
ALARM			
CLOTHES/BACKPACK			
GLASS OF WATER			
SAVERS PREP			
BEDTIME AFFIRMATIONS			

Wednesday	Thursday	Friday	Saturday
S	S	S	S
A	A	A	A
V	V	V	V
E	E	E	E
R	R	R	R
S	S	S	S
◆	◆	◆	◆
◆	◆	◆	◆

Wednesday		Thursday		Friday		Saturday	
5:00		5:00		5:00		5:00	
5:30		5:30		5:30		5:30	
6:00		6:00		6:00		6:00	
6:30		6:30		6:30		6:30	
7:00		7:00		7:00		7:00	
7:30		7:30		7:30		7:30	
8:00		8:00		8:00		8:00	
8:30		8:30		8:30		8:30	
9:00		9:00		9:00		9:00	
9:30		9:30		9:30		9:30	
10:00		10:00		10:00		10:00	
10:30		10:30		10:30		10:30	
11:00		11:00		11:00		11:00	
11:30		11:30		11:30		11:30	
12:00		12:00		12:00		12:00	
12:30		12:30		12:30		12:30	
1:00		1:00		1:00		1:00	
1:30		1:30		1:30		1:30	
2:00		2:00		2:00		2:00	
2:30		2:30		2:30		2:30	
3:00		3:00		3:00		3:00	
3:30		3:30		3:30		3:30	
4:00		4:00		4:00		4:00	
4:30		4:30		4:30		4:30	
5:00		5:00		5:00		5:00	
5:30		5:30		5:30		5:30	
6:00		6:00		6:00		6:00	
6:30		6:30		6:30		6:30	
7:00		7:00		7:00		7:00	
7:30		7:30		7:30		7:30	
8:00		8:00		8:00		8:00	
8:30		8:30		8:30		8:30	
9:00		9:00		9:00		9:00	
9:30		9:30		9:30		9:30	
10:00		10:00		10:00		10:00	
10:30		10:30		10:30		10:30	
11:00		11:00		11:00		11:00	
( )		( )		( )		( )	

WEEKLY REFLECTION

• •

1) What was my greatest accomplishment this week?

2) Who or what am I grateful for?

3) What activity from this last week took away from my focus and time?

4) What is one thing I can do to be better prepared for this week?

5) What am I looking forward to during the upcoming week?

BRAINSTORM

FINANCIAL CHECKBOX

Questions	Yes	No
Did I remain on budget this week?		
Did I buy what I needed over what I wanted?		
If you got paid this week, did you place 10% of it in your savings?		
Have I taken a percentage (1%-10%) to donate?		
Did I use my credit card wisely this week?		

How can I manage my money more wisely this week?

MONTHLY REFLECTION

....

Write 5 things you accomplished this month:

1.

2.

3.

4.

5.

QUESTIONS

1) What did I learn about myself this month?

2) What tasks are left over from this month that are lingering and need to get done?

3. Did I take care of myself?

4) What could I have done differently this past month?

5) What areas can I (still) improve on?

6) What experiences can I treasure?

7) What challenged me and how did I overcome the challenge?

8) What specific habits and/or rituals could I develop this month to support my vision?

You are always exactly where you are supposed to be, experiencing what you need to experience, to learn what you must learn, in order to become the person you need to be to create the life you truly want. Always.

- HAL ELROD

DREAMS

· ·

Write out your dreams below ...

VISION BOARD

• •

Paste or draw pictures of your visions ...

MONTH OF:	SUNDAY	MONDAY	TUESDAY
This Month's Goal			
Important Events or Reminders to Transfer to My Phone			
1.			
2.			
3.			
4.			
5.			
6.			
7.			
8.			
9.			
10.			

PROJECT NAME	CLASS & INSTRUCTOR	IMPORTANT DATES	DEADLINES
1.			
2.			
3.			
4.			

WEDNESDAY	THURSDAY	FRIDAY	SATURDAY

BRAINSTORM

Week of:	Sunday	Monday	Tuesday
This Week's Goal	S	S	S
	A	A	A
	V	V	V
	E	E	E
	R	R	R
	S	S	S
Intention for the Day	◆	◆	◆
Grateful for ...	◆	◆	◆

Where you are is a result of who you were, where you go depends entirely on the person you choose to be from this moment forward.

—HAL ELROD

TO-DO LIST
Highest Priority
Definite Priority
Lowest Priority
Habit to Work on This Week

Time	Sunday	Monday	Tuesday
5:00			
5:30			
6:00			
6:30			
7:00			
7:30			
8:00			
8:30			
9:00			
9:30			
10:00			
10:30			
11:00			
11:30			
12:00			
12:30			
1:00			
1:30			
2:00			
2:30			
3:00			
3:30			
4:00			
4:30			
5:00			
5:30			
6:00			
6:30			
7:00			
7:30			
8:00			
8:30			
9:00			
9:30			
10:00			
10:30			
11:00			

Ready for tomorrow?	( )	( )	( )
ALARM			
CLOTHES/BACKPACK			
GLASS OF WATER			
SAVERS PREP			
BEDTIME AFFIRMATIONS			

Wednesday	Thursday	Friday	Saturday
S	S	S	S
A	A	A	A
V	V	V	V
E	E	E	E
R	R	R	R
S	S	S	S
◆	◆	◆	◆
◆	◆	◆	◆

Wednesday	Thursday	Friday	Saturday
5:00	5:00	5:00	5:00
5:30	5:30	5:30	5:30
6:00	6:00	6:00	6:00
6:30	6:30	6:30	6:30
7:00	7:00	7:00	7:00
7:30	7:30	7:30	7:30
8:00	8:00	8:00	8:00
8:30	8:30	8:30	8:30
9:00	9:00	9:00	9:00
9:30	9:30	9:30	9:30
10:00	10:00	10:00	10:00
10:30	10:30	10:30	10:30
11:00	11:00	11:00	11:00
11:30	11:30	11:30	11:30
12:00	12:00	12:00	12:00
12:30	12:30	12:30	12:30
1:00	1:00	1:00	1:00
1:30	1:30	1:30	1:30
2:00	2:00	2:00	2:00
2:30	2:30	2:30	2:30
3:00	3:00	3:00	3:00
3:30	3:30	3:30	3:30
4:00	4:00	4:00	4:00
4:30	4:30	4:30	4:30
5:00	5:00	5:00	5:00
5:30	5:30	5:30	5:30
6:00	6:00	6:00	6:00
6:30	6:30	6:30	6:30
7:00	7:00	7:00	7:00
7:30	7:30	7:30	7:30
8:00	8:00	8:00	8:00
8:30	8:30	8:30	8:30
9:00	9:00	9:00	9:00
9:30	9:30	9:30	9:30
10:00	10:00	10:00	10:00
10:30	10:30	10:30	10:30
11:00	11:00	11:00	11:00
( )	( )	( )	( )

WEEKLY REFLECTION

....

1) What was my greatest accomplishment this week?

2) Who or what am I grateful for?

3) What activity from this last week took away from my focus and time?

4) What is one thing I can do to be better prepared for this week?

5) What am I looking forward to during the upcoming week?

BRAINSTORM

FINANCIAL CHECKBOX

Questions	Yes	No
Did I remain on budget this week?		
Did I buy what I needed over what I wanted?		
If you got paid this week, did you place 10% of it in your savings?		
Have I taken a percentage (1%-10%) to donate?		
Did I use my credit card wisely this week?		
How can I manage my money more wisely this week?		

Week of:	Sunday	Monday	Tuesday
This Week's Goal	S	S	S
	A	A	A
	V	V	V
	E	E	E
	R	R	R
	S	S	S
Intention for the Day	◆	◆	◆
Grateful for ...	◆	◆	◆

The successful warrior is the average man, with laser-like focus.

—BRUCE LEE

TO-DO LIST

Highest Priority

Definite Priority

Lowest Priority

Habit to Work on This Week

	Sunday	Monday	Tuesday
5:00		5:00		5:00	
5:30		5:30		5:30	
6:00		6:00		6:00	
6:30		6:30		6:30	
7:00		7:00		7:00	
7:30		7:30		7:30	
8:00		8:00		8:00	
8:30		8:30		8:30	
9:00		9:00		9:00	
9:30		9:30		9:30	
10:00		10:00		10:00	
10:30		10:30		10:30	
11:00		11:00		11:00	
11:30		11:30		11:30	
12:00		12:00		12:00	
12:30		12:30		12:30	
1:00		1:00		1:00	
1:30		1:30		1:30	
2:00		2:00		2:00	
2:30		2:30		2:30	
3:00		3:00		3:00	
3:30		3:30		3:30	
4:00		4:00		4:00	
4:30		4:30		4:30	
5:00		5:00		5:00	
5:30		5:30		5:30	
6:00		6:00		6:00	
6:30		6:30		6:30	
7:00		7:00		7:00	
7:30		7:30		7:30	
8:00		8:00		8:00	
8:30		8:30		8:30	
9:00		9:00		9:00	
9:30		9:30		9:30	
10:00		10:00		10:00	
10:30		10:30		10:30	
11:00		11:00		11:00	

Ready for tomorrow?	( )	( )	( )
ALARM			
CLOTHES/BACKPACK			
GLASS OF WATER			
SAVERS PREP			
BEDTIME AFFIRMATIONS			

Wednesday		Thursday		Friday		Saturday	
S		S		S		S	
A		A		A		A	
V		V		V		V	
E		E		E		E	
R		R		R		R	
S		S		S		S	
◆		◆		◆		◆	
◆		◆		◆		◆	
5:00		5:00		5:00		5:00	
5:30		5:30		5:30		5:30	
6:00		6:00		6:00		6:00	
6:30		6:30		6:30		6:30	
7:00		7:00		7:00		7:00	
7:30		7:30		7:30		7:30	
8:00		8:00		8:00		8:00	
8:30		8:30		8:30		8:30	
9:00		9:00		9:00		9:00	
9:30		9:30		9:30		9:30	
10:00		10:00		10:00		10:00	
10:30		10:30		10:30		10:30	
11:00		11:00		11:00		11:00	
11:30		11:30		11:30		11:30	
12:00		12:00		12:00		12:00	
12:30		12:30		12:30		12:30	
1:00		1:00		1:00		1:00	
1:30		1:30		1:30		1:30	
2:00		2:00		2:00		2:00	
2:30		2:30		2:30		2:30	
3:00		3:00		3:00		3:00	
3:30		3:30		3:30		3:30	
4:00		4:00		4:00		4:00	
4:30		4:30		4:30		4:30	
5:00		5:00		5:00		5:00	
5:30		5:30		5:30		5:30	
6:00		6:00		6:00		6:00	
6:30		6:30		6:30		6:30	
7:00		7:00		7:00		7:00	
7:30		7:30		7:30		7:30	
8:00		8:00		8:00		8:00	
8:30		8:30		8:30		8:30	
9:00		9:00		9:00		9:00	
9:30		9:30		9:30		9:30	
10:00		10:00		10:00		10:00	
10:30		10:30		10:30		10:30	
11:00		11:00		11:00		11:00	
	( )		( )		( )		( )

WEEKLY REFLECTION

....

1) What was my greatest accomplishment this week?

2) Who or what am I grateful for?

3) What activity from this last week took away from my focus and time?

4) What is one thing I can do to be better prepared for this week?

5) What am I looking forward to during the upcoming week?

BRAINSTORM

FINANCIAL CHECKBOX

Questions	Yes	No
Did I remain on budget this week?		
Did I buy what I needed over what I wanted?		
If you got paid this week, did you place 10% of it in your savings?		
Have I taken a percentage (1%-10%) to donate?		
Did I use my credit card wisely this week?		

How can I manage my money more wisely this week?

Week of:	Sunday	Monday	Tuesday
This Week's Goal	S	S	S
	A	A	A
	V	V	V
	E	E	E
	R	R	R
	S	S	S
Intention for the Day	◆	◆	◆
Grateful for ...	◆	◆	◆

We make a living by what we get. We make a life by what we give.

—WINSTON CHURCHILL

	Sunday	Monday	Tuesday
TO-DO LIST	5:00	5:00	5:00
Highest Priority	5:30	5:30	5:30
	6:00	6:00	6:00
	6:30	6:30	6:30
	7:00	7:00	7:00
	7:30	7:30	7:30
	8:00	8:00	8:00
	8:30	8:30	8:30
	9:00	9:00	9:00
	9:30	9:30	9:30
	10:00	10:00	10:00
	10:30	10:30	10:30
	11:00	11:00	11:00
	11:30	11:30	11:30
	12:00	12:00	12:00
	12:30	12:30	12:30
	1:00	1:00	1:00
Definite Priority	1:30	1:30	1:30
	2:00	2:00	2:00
	2:30	2:30	2:30
	3:00	3:00	3:00
	3:30	3:30	3:30
	4:00	4:00	4:00
Lowest Priority	4:30	4:30	4:30
	5:00	5:00	5:00
	5:30	5:30	5:30
	6:00	6:00	6:00
	6:30	6:30	6:30
	7:00	7:00	7:00
	7:30	7:30	7:30
Habit to Work on This Week	8:00	8:00	8:00
	8:30	8:30	8:30
	9:00	9:00	9:00
	9:30	9:30	9:30
	10:00	10:00	10:00
	10:30	10:30	10:30
	11:00	11:00	11:00

Ready for tomorrow?	( )	( )	( )
ALARM			
CLOTHES/BACKPACK			
GLASS OF WATER			
SAVERS PREP			
BEDTIME AFFIRMATIONS			

Wednesday		Thursday		Friday		Saturday	
S		S		S		S	
A		A		A		A	
V		V		V		V	
E		E		E		E	
R		R		R		R	
S		S		S		S	
◆		◆		◆		◆	
◆		◆		◆		◆	

Wednesday	Thursday	Friday	Saturday
5:00	5:00	5:00	5:00
5:30	5:30	5:30	5:30
6:00	6:00	6:00	6:00
6:30	6:30	6:30	6:30
7:00	7:00	7:00	7:00
7:30	7:30	7:30	7:30
8:00	8:00	8:00	8:00
8:30	8:30	8:30	8:30
9:00	9:00	9:00	9:00
9:30	9:30	9:30	9:30
10:00	10:00	10:00	10:00
10:30	10:30	10:30	10:30
11:00	11:00	11:00	11:00
11:30	11:30	11:30	11:30
12:00	12:00	12:00	12:00
12:30	12:30	12:30	12:30
1:00	1:00	1:00	1:00
1:30	1:30	1:30	1:30
2:00	2:00	2:00	2:00
2:30	2:30	2:30	2:30
3:00	3:00	3:00	3:00
3:30	3:30	3:30	3:30
4:00	4:00	4:00	4:00
4:30	4:30	4:30	4:30
5:00	5:00	5:00	5:00
5:30	5:30	5:30	5:30
6:00	6:00	6:00	6:00
6:30	6:30	6:30	6:30
7:00	7:00	7:00	7:00
7:30	7:30	7:30	7:30
8:00	8:00	8:00	8:00
8:30	8:30	8:30	8:30
9:00	9:00	9:00	9:00
9:30	9:30	9:30	9:30
10:00	10:00	10:00	10:00
10:30	10:30	10:30	10:30
11:00	11:00	11:00	11:00

( )	( )	( )	( )

WEEKLY REFLECTION

....

1) What was my greatest accomplishment this week?

2) Who or what am I grateful for?

3) What activity from this last week took away from my focus and time?

4) What is one thing I can do to be better prepared for this week?

5) What am I looking forward to during the upcoming week?

BRAINSTORM

FINANCIAL CHECKBOX

Questions	Yes	No
Did I remain on budget this week?		
Did I buy what I needed over what I wanted?		
If you got paid this week, did you place 10% of it in your savings?		
Have I taken a percentage (1%-10%) to donate?		
Did I use my credit card wisely this week?		

How can I manage my money more wisely this week?

Week of:	Sunday	Monday	Tuesday
This Week's Goal	S	S	S
	A	A	A
	V	V	V
	E	E	E
	R	R	R
	S	S	S
Intention for the Day	◆	◆	◆
Grateful for ...	◆	◆	◆

	Sunday	Monday	Tuesday
	5:00	5:00	5:00
	5:30	5:30	5:30
	6:00	6:00	6:00
Dream Big. Work Hard.	6:30	6:30	6:30
Create Value.	7:00	7:00	7:00
	7:30	7:30	7:30
— JEFF HOFFMAN	8:00	8:00	8:00
	8:30	8:30	8:30
	9:00	9:00	9:00
	9:30	9:30	9:30
TO-DO LIST	10:00	10:00	10:00
Highest Priority	10:30	10:30	10:30
	11:00	11:00	11:00
	11:30	11:30	11:30
	12:00	12:00	12:00
	12:30	12:30	12:30
	1:00	1:00	1:00
Definite Priority	1:30	1:30	1:30
	2:00	2:00	2:00
	2:30	2:30	2:30
	3:00	3:00	3:00
	3:30	3:30	3:30
	4:00	4:00	4:00
Lowest Priority	4:30	4:30	4:30
	5:00	5:00	5:00
	5:30	5:30	5:30
	6:00	6:00	6:00
	6:30	6:30	6:30
	7:00	7:00	7:00
	7:30	7:30	7:30
Habit to Work on This Week	8:00	8:00	8:00
	8:30	8:30	8:30
	9:00	9:00	9:00
	9:30	9:30	9:30
	10:00	10:00	10:00
	10:30	10:30	10:30
	11:00	11:00	11:00

Ready for tomorrow?	( )	( )	( )
ALARM			
CLOTHES/BACKPACK			
GLASS OF WATER			
SAVERS PREP			
BEDTIME AFFIRMATIONS			

Wednesday	Thursday	Friday	Saturday
S	S	S	S
A	A	A	A
V	V	V	V
E	E	E	E
R	R	R	R
S	S	S	S
◆	◆	◆	◆
◆	◆	◆	◆

Wednesday	Thursday	Friday	Saturday
5:00	5:00	5:00	5:00
5:30	5:30	5:30	5:30
6:00	6:00	6:00	6:00
6:30	6:30	6:30	6:30
7:00	7:00	7:00	7:00
7:30	7:30	7:30	7:30
8:00	8:00	8:00	8:00
8:30	8:30	8:30	8:30
9:00	9:00	9:00	9:00
9:30	9:30	9:30	9:30
10:00	10:00	10:00	10:00
10:30	10:30	10:30	10:30
11:00	11:00	11:00	11:00
11:30	11:30	11:30	11:30
12:00	12:00	12:00	12:00
12:30	12:30	12:30	12:30
1:00	1:00	1:00	1:00
1:30	1:30	1:30	1:30
2:00	2:00	2:00	2:00
2:30	2:30	2:30	2:30
3:00	3:00	3:00	3:00
3:30	3:30	3:30	3:30
4:00	4:00	4:00	4:00
4:30	4:30	4:30	4:30
5:00	5:00	5:00	5:00
5:30	5:30	5:30	5:30
6:00	6:00	6:00	6:00
6:30	6:30	6:30	6:30
7:00	7:00	7:00	7:00
7:30	7:30	7:30	7:30
8:00	8:00	8:00	8:00
8:30	8:30	8:30	8:30
9:00	9:00	9:00	9:00
9:30	9:30	9:30	9:30
10:00	10:00	10:00	10:00
10:30	10:30	10:30	10:30
11:00	11:00	11:00	11:00

( )	( )	( )	( )

WEEKLY REFLECTION

• •

1) What was my greatest accomplishment this week?

2) Who or what am I grateful for?

3) What activity from this last week took away from my focus and time?

4) What is one thing I can do to be better prepared for this week?

5) What am I looking forward to during the upcoming week?

BRAINSTORM

FINANCIAL CHECKBOX

Questions	Yes	No
Did I remain on budget this week?		
Did I buy what I needed over what I wanted?		
If you got paid this week, did you place 10% of it in your savings?		
Have I taken a percentage (1%-10%) to donate?		
Did I use my credit card wisely this week?		

How can I manage my money more wisely this week?

Week of:	Sunday		Monday		Tuesday	
This Week's Goal	S		S		S	
	A		A		A	
	V		V		V	
	E		E		E	
	R		R		R	
	S		S		S	
Intention for the Day	◆		◆		◆	
Grateful for ...	◆		◆		◆	

	Sunday	Monday	Tuesday
Why not go out on a limb? That's where the fruit it is. —**MARK TWAIN**	5:00	5:00	5:00
	5:30	5:30	5:30
	6:00	6:00	6:00
	6:30	6:30	6:30
	7:00	7:00	7:00
	7:30	7:30	7:30
	8:00	8:00	8:00
	8:30	8:30	8:30
	9:00	9:00	9:00
	9:30	9:30	9:30
TO-DO LIST	10:00	10:00	10:00
Highest Priority	10:30	10:30	10:30
	11:00	11:00	11:00
	11:30	11:30	11:30
	12:00	12:00	12:00
	12:30	12:30	12:30
	1:00	1:00	1:00
Definite Priority	1:30	1:30	1:30
	2:00	2:00	2:00
	2:30	2:30	2:30
	3:00	3:00	3:00
	3:30	3:30	3:30
	4:00	4:00	4:00
Lowest Priority	4:30	4:30	4:30
	5:00	5:00	5:00
	5:30	5:30	5:30
	6:00	6:00	6:00
	6:30	6:30	6:30
	7:00	7:00	7:00
	7:30	7:30	7:30
Habit to Work on This Week	8:00	8:00	8:00
	8:30	8:30	8:30
	9:00	9:00	9:00
	9:30	9:30	9:30
	10:00	10:00	10:00
	10:30	10:30	10:30
	11:00	11:00	11:00

Ready for tomorrow?	( )	( )	( )
ALARM			
CLOTHES/BACKPACK			
GLASS OF WATER			
SAVERS PREP			
BEDTIME AFFIRMATIONS			

Wednesday		Thursday		Friday		Saturday	
S		S		S		S	
A		A		A		A	
V		V		V		V	
E		E		E		E	
R		R		R		R	
S		S		S		S	

◆		◆		◆		◆	
◆		◆		◆		◆	

Wednesday	Thursday	Friday	Saturday
5:00	5:00	5:00	5:00
5:30	5:30	5:30	5:30
6:00	6:00	6:00	6:00
6:30	6:30	6:30	6:30
7:00	7:00	7:00	7:00
7:30	7:30	7:30	7:30
8:00	8:00	8:00	8:00
8:30	8:30	8:30	8:30
9:00	9:00	9:00	9:00
9:30	9:30	9:30	9:30
10:00	10:00	10:00	10:00
10:30	10:30	10:30	10:30
11:00	11:00	11:00	11:00
11:30	11:30	11:30	11:30
12:00	12:00	12:00	12:00
12:30	12:30	12:30	12:30
1:00	1:00	1:00	1:00
1:30	1:30	1:30	1:30
2:00	2:00	2:00	2:00
2:30	2:30	2:30	2:30
3:00	3:00	3:00	3:00
3:30	3:30	3:30	3:30
4:00	4:00	4:00	4:00
4:30	4:30	4:30	4:30
5:00	5:00	5:00	5:00
5:30	5:30	5:30	5:30
6:00	6:00	6:00	6:00
6:30	6:30	6:30	6:30
7:00	7:00	7:00	7:00
7:30	7:30	7:30	7:30
8:00	8:00	8:00	8:00
8:30	8:30	8:30	8:30
9:00	9:00	9:00	9:00
9:30	9:30	9:30	9:30
10:00	10:00	10:00	10:00
10:30	10:30	10:30	10:30
11:00	11:00	11:00	11:00

( )	( )	( )	( )

WEEKLY REFLECTION

● ●

1) What was my greatest accomplishment this week?

2) Who or what am I grateful for?

3) What activity from this last week took away from my focus and time?

4) What is one thing I can do to be better prepared for this week?

5) What am I looking forward to during the upcoming week?

BRAINSTORM

FINANCIAL CHECKBOX

Questions	Yes	No
Did I remain on budget this week?		
Did I buy what I needed over what I wanted?		
If you got paid this week, did you place 10% of it in your savings?		
Have I taken a percentage (1%-10%) to donate?		
Did I use my credit card wisely this week?		

How can I manage my money more wisely this week?

MONTHLY REFLECTION

· ·

Write 5 things you accomplished this month:

1.

2.

3.

4.

5.

QUESTIONS

1) What did I learn about myself this month?

2) What tasks are left over from this month that are lingering and need to get done?

3. Did I take care of myself?

4) What could I have done differently this past month?

5) What areas can I (still) improve on?

6) What experiences can I treasure?

7) What challenged me and how did I overcome the challenge?

8) What specific habits and/or rituals could I develop this month to support my vision?

MONTH OF:	SUNDAY	MONDAY	TUESDAY
This Month's Goal			
Important Events or Reminders to Transfer to My Phone			
1.			
2.			
3.			
4.			
5.			
6.			
7.			
8.			
9.			
10.			

PROJECT NAME	CLASS & INSTRUCTOR	IMPORTANT DATES	DEADLINES
1.			
2.			
3.			
4.			

WEDNESDAY	THURSDAY	FRIDAY	SATURDAY

BRAINSTORM

Week of:	Sunday	Monday	Tuesday
This Week's Goal	S	S	S
	A	A	A
	V	V	V
	E	E	E
	R	R	R
	S	S	S
Intention for the Day	◆	◆	◆
Grateful for ...	◆	◆	◆

Whatever the mind of man can conceive and believe, it can achieve.

—NAPOLEON HILL

TO-DO LIST
Highest Priority
Definite Priority
Lowest Priority
Habit to Work on This Week

Time	Sunday	Time	Monday	Time	Tuesday
5:00		5:00		5:00	
5:30		5:30		5:30	
6:00		6:00		6:00	
6:30		6:30		6:30	
7:00		7:00		7:00	
7:30		7:30		7:30	
8:00		8:00		8:00	
8:30		8:30		8:30	
9:00		9:00		9:00	
9:30		9:30		9:30	
10:00		10:00		10:00	
10:30		10:30		10:30	
11:00		11:00		11:00	
11:30		11:30		11:30	
12:00		12:00		12:00	
12:30		12:30		12:30	
1:00		1:00		1:00	
1:30		1:30		1:30	
2:00		2:00		2:00	
2:30		2:30		2:30	
3:00		3:00		3:00	
3:30		3:30		3:30	
4:00		4:00		4:00	
4:30		4:30		4:30	
5:00		5:00		5:00	
5:30		5:30		5:30	
6:00		6:00		6:00	
6:30		6:30		6:30	
7:00		7:00		7:00	
7:30		7:30		7:30	
8:00		8:00		8:00	
8:30		8:30		8:30	
9:00		9:00		9:00	
9:30		9:30		9:30	
10:00		10:00		10:00	
10:30		10:30		10:30	
11:00		11:00		11:00	

Ready for tomorrow?	( )	( )	( )
ALARM			
CLOTHES/BACKPACK			
GLASS OF WATER			
SAVERS PREP			
BEDTIME AFFIRMATIONS			

Wednesday		Thursday		Friday		Saturday	
S		S		S		S	
A		A		A		A	
V		V		V		V	
E		E		E		E	
R		R		R		R	
S		S		S		S	
◆		◆		◆		◆	
◆		◆		◆		◆	
5:00		5:00		5:00		5:00	
5:30		5:30		5:30		5:30	
6:00		6:00		6:00		6:00	
6:30		6:30		6:30		6:30	
7:00		7:00		7:00		7:00	
7:30		7:30		7:30		7:30	
8:00		8:00		8:00		8:00	
8:30		8:30		8:30		8:30	
9:00		9:00		9:00		9:00	
9:30		9:30		9:30		9:30	
10:00		10:00		10:00		10:00	
10:30		10:30		10:30		10:30	
11:00		11:00		11:00		11:00	
11:30		11:30		11:30		11:30	
12:00		12:00		12:00		12:00	
12:30		12:30		12:30		12:30	
1:00		1:00		1:00		1:00	
1:30		1:30		1:30		1:30	
2:00		2:00		2:00		2:00	
2:30		2:30		2:30		2:30	
3:00		3:00		3:00		3:00	
3:30		3:30		3:30		3:30	
4:00		4:00		4:00		4:00	
4:30		4:30		4:30		4:30	
5:00		5:00		5:00		5:00	
5:30		5:30		5:30		5:30	
6:00		6:00		6:00		6:00	
6:30		6:30		6:30		6:30	
7:00		7:00		7:00		7:00	
7:30		7:30		7:30		7:30	
8:00		8:00		8:00		8:00	
8:30		8:30		8:30		8:30	
9:00		9:00		9:00		9:00	
9:30		9:30		9:30		9:30	
10:00		10:00		10:00		10:00	
10:30		10:30		10:30		10:30	
11:00		11:00		11:00		11:00	
	( )		( )		( )		( )

WEEKLY REFLECTION

• •

1) What was my greatest accomplishment this week?

2) Who or what am I grateful for?

3) What activity from this last week took away from my focus and time?

4) What is one thing I can do to be better prepared for this week?

5) What am I looking forward to during the upcoming week?

BRAINSTORM

FINANCIAL CHECKBOX

Questions	Yes	No
Did I remain on budget this week?		
Did I buy what I needed over what I wanted?		
If you got paid this week, did you place 10% of it in your savings?		
Have I taken a percentage (1%-10%) to donate?		
Did I use my credit card wisely this week?		

How can I manage my money more wisely this week?

Week of:	Sunday		Monday		Tuesday	
This Week's Goal	S		S		S	
	A		A		A	
	V		V		V	
	E		E		E	
	R		R		R	
	S		S		S	
Intention for the Day	◆		◆		◆	
Grateful for …	◆		◆		◆	

		Sunday		Monday		Tuesday
Strive not to be a success, but rather to be of value. —ALBERT EINSTEIN	5:00		5:00		5:00	
	5:30		5:30		5:30	
	6:00		6:00		6:00	
	6:30		6:30		6:30	
	7:00		7:00		7:00	
	7:30		7:30		7:30	
	8:00		8:00		8:00	
	8:30		8:30		8:30	
	9:00		9:00		9:00	
	9:30		9:30		9:30	
TO-DO LIST	10:00		10:00		10:00	
Highest Priority	10:30		10:30		10:30	
	11:00		11:00		11:00	
	11:30		11:30		11:30	
	12:00		12:00		12:00	
	12:30		12:30		12:30	
	1:00		1:00		1:00	
Definite Priority	1:30		1:30		1:30	
	2:00		2:00		2:00	
	2:30		2:30		2:30	
	3:00		3:00		3:00	
	3:30		3:30		3:30	
	4:00		4:00		4:00	
Lowest Priority	4:30		4:30		4:30	
	5:00		5:00		5:00	
	5:30		5:30		5:30	
	6:00		6:00		6:00	
	6:30		6:30		6:30	
	7:00		7:00		7:00	
	7:30		7:30		7:30	
Habit to Work on This Week	8:00		8:00		8:00	
	8:30		8:30		8:30	
	9:00		9:00		9:00	
	9:30		9:30		9:30	
	10:00		10:00		10:00	
	10:30		10:30		10:30	
	11:00		11:00		11:00	

Ready for tomorrow?		( )		( )		( )
ALARM						
CLOTHES/BACKPACK						
GLASS OF WATER						
SAVERS PREP						
BEDTIME AFFIRMATIONS						

Wednesday		Thursday		Friday		Saturday	
S		S		S		S	
A		A		A		A	
V		V		V		V	
E		E		E		E	
R		R		R		R	
S		S		S		S	
◆		◆		◆		◆	
◆		◆		◆		◆	
5:00		5:00		5:00		5:00	
5:30		5:30		5:30		5:30	
6:00		6:00		6:00		6:00	
6:30		6:30		6:30		6:30	
7:00		7:00		7:00		7:00	
7:30		7:30		7:30		7:30	
8:00		8:00		8:00		8:00	
8:30		8:30		8:30		8:30	
9:00		9:00		9:00		9:00	
9:30		9:30		9:30		9:30	
10:00		10:00		10:00		10:00	
10:30		10:30		10:30		10:30	
11:00		11:00		11:00		11:00	
11:30		11:30		11:30		11:30	
12:00		12:00		12:00		12:00	
12:30		12:30		12:30		12:30	
1:00		1:00		1:00		1:00	
1:30		1:30		1:30		1:30	
2:00		2:00		2:00		2:00	
2:30		2:30		2:30		2:30	
3:00		3:00		3:00		3:00	
3:30		3:30		3:30		3:30	
4:00		4:00		4:00		4:00	
4:30		4:30		4:30		4:30	
5:00		5:00		5:00		5:00	
5:30		5:30		5:30		5:30	
6:00		6:00		6:00		6:00	
6:30		6:30		6:30		6:30	
7:00		7:00		7:00		7:00	
7:30		7:30		7:30		7:30	
8:00		8:00		8:00		8:00	
8:30		8:30		8:30		8:30	
9:00		9:00		9:00		9:00	
9:30		9:30		9:30		9:30	
10:00		10:00		10:00		10:00	
10:30		10:30		10:30		10:30	
11:00		11:00		11:00		11:00	
( )		( )		( )		( )	

WEEKLY REFLECTION

• •

1) What was my greatest accomplishment this week?

2) Who or what am I grateful for?

3) What activity from this last week took away from my focus and time?

4) What is one thing I can do to be better prepared for this week?

5) What am I looking forward to during the upcoming week?

BRAINSTORM

FINANCIAL CHECKBOX

Questions	Yes	No
Did I remain on budget this week?		
Did I buy what I needed over what I wanted?		
If you got paid this week, did you place 10% of it in your savings?		
Have I taken a percentage (1%-10%) to donate?		
Did I use my credit card wisely this week?		

How can I manage my money more wisely this week?

Week of:	Sunday	Monday	Tuesday
This Week's Goal	S	S	S
	A	A	A
	V	V	V
	E	E	E
	R	R	R
	S	S	S
Intention for the Day	◆	◆	◆
Grateful for ...	◆	◆	◆

Life is what happens to you while you're busy making other plans.

—JOHN LENNON

TO-DO LIST
Highest Priority
Definite Priority
Lowest Priority
Habit to Work on This Week

Time	Sunday	Monday	Tuesday
5:00		5:00	5:00
5:30		5:30	5:30
6:00		6:00	6:00
6:30		6:30	6:30
7:00		7:00	7:00
7:30		7:30	7:30
8:00		8:00	8:00
8:30		8:30	8:30
9:00		9:00	9:00
9:30		9:30	9:30
10:00		10:00	10:00
10:30		10:30	10:30
11:00		11:00	11:00
11:30		11:30	11:30
12:00		12:00	12:00
12:30		12:30	12:30
1:00		1:00	1:00
1:30		1:30	1:30
2:00		2:00	2:00
2:30		2:30	2:30
3:00		3:00	3:00
3:30		3:30	3:30
4:00		4:00	4:00
4:30		4:30	4:30
5:00		5:00	5:00
5:30		5:30	5:30
6:00		6:00	6:00
6:30		6:30	6:30
7:00		7:00	7:00
7:30		7:30	7:30
8:00		8:00	8:00
8:30		8:30	8:30
9:00		9:00	9:00
9:30		9:30	9:30
10:00		10:00	10:00
10:30		10:30	10:30
11:00		11:00	11:00

Ready for tomorrow?	( )	( )	( )
ALARM			
CLOTHES/BACKPACK			
GLASS OF WATER			
SAVERS PREP			
BEDTIME AFFIRMATIONS			

Wednesday	Thursday	Friday	Saturday
S	S	S	S
A	A	A	A
V	V	V	V
E	E	E	E
R	R	R	R
S	S	S	S

◆	◆	◆	◆
◆	◆	◆	◆

Wednesday	Thursday	Friday	Saturday
5:00	5:00	5:00	5:00
5:30	5:30	5:30	5:30
6:00	6:00	6:00	6:00
6:30	6:30	6:30	6:30
7:00	7:00	7:00	7:00
7:30	7:30	7:30	7:30
8:00	8:00	8:00	8:00
8:30	8:30	8:30	8:30
9:00	9:00	9:00	9:00
9:30	9:30	9:30	9:30
10:00	10:00	10:00	10:00
10:30	10:30	10:30	10:30
11:00	11:00	11:00	11:00
11:30	11:30	11:30	11:30
12:00	12:00	12:00	12:00
12:30	12:30	12:30	12:30
1:00	1:00	1:00	1:00
1:30	1:30	1:30	1:30
2:00	2:00	2:00	2:00
2:30	2:30	2:30	2:30
3:00	3:00	3:00	3:00
3:30	3:30	3:30	3:30
4:00	4:00	4:00	4:00
4:30	4:30	4:30	4:30
5:00	5:00	5:00	5:00
5:30	5:30	5:30	5:30
6:00	6:00	6:00	6:00
6:30	6:30	6:30	6:30
7:00	7:00	7:00	7:00
7:30	7:30	7:30	7:30
8:00	8:00	8:00	8:00
8:30	8:30	8:30	8:30
9:00	9:00	9:00	9:00
9:30	9:30	9:30	9:30
10:00	10:00	10:00	10:00
10:30	10:30	10:30	10:30
11:00	11:00	11:00	11:00

( )	( )	( )	( )

WEEKLY REFLECTION

....

1) What was my greatest accomplishment this week?

2) Who or what am I grateful for?

3) What activity from this last week took away from my focus and time?

4) What is one thing I can do to be better prepared for this week?

5) What am I looking forward to during the upcoming week?

BRAINSTORM

FINANCIAL CHECKBOX

Questions	Yes	No
Did I remain on budget this week?		
Did I buy what I needed over what I wanted?		
If you got paid this week, did you place 10% of it in your savings?		
Have I taken a percentage (1%-10%) to donate?		
Did I use my credit card wisely this week?		

How can I manage my money more wisely this week?

Week of:	Sunday	Monday	Tuesday
This Week's Goal	S	S	S
	A	A	A
	V	V	V
	E	E	E
	R	R	R
	S	S	S
Intention for the Day	◆	◆	◆
Grateful for …	◆	◆	◆

Your time is limited, so don't waste it living someone else's life.

—STEVE JOBS

TO-DO LIST			
Highest Priority			
Definite Priority			
Lowest Priority			
Habit to Work on This Week			

Time	Sunday	Monday	Tuesday
5:00		5:00	5:00
5:30		5:30	5:30
6:00		6:00	6:00
6:30		6:30	6:30
7:00		7:00	7:00
7:30		7:30	7:30
8:00		8:00	8:00
8:30		8:30	8:30
9:00		9:00	9:00
9:30		9:30	9:30
10:00		10:00	10:00
10:30		10:30	10:30
11:00		11:00	11:00
11:30		11:30	11:30
12:00		12:00	12:00
12:30		12:30	12:30
1:00		1:00	1:00
1:30		1:30	1:30
2:00		2:00	2:00
2:30		2:30	2:30
3:00		3:00	3:00
3:30		3:30	3:30
4:00		4:00	4:00
4:30		4:30	4:30
5:00		5:00	5:00
5:30		5:30	5:30
6:00		6:00	6:00
6:30		6:30	6:30
7:00		7:00	7:00
7:30		7:30	7:30
8:00		8:00	8:00
8:30		8:30	8:30
9:00		9:00	9:00
9:30		9:30	9:30
10:00		10:00	10:00
10:30		10:30	10:30
11:00		11:00	11:00

Ready for tomorrow?	( )	( )	( )
ALARM			
CLOTHES/BACKPACK			
GLASS OF WATER			
SAVERS PREP			
BEDTIME AFFIRMATIONS			

Wednesday		Thursday		Friday		Saturday	
S		S		S		S	
A		A		A		A	
V		V		V		V	
E		E		E		E	
R		R		R		R	
S		S		S		S	
◆		◆		◆		◆	
◆		◆		◆		◆	
5:00		5:00		5:00		5:00	
5:30		5:30		5:30		5:30	
6:00		6:00		6:00		6:00	
6:30		6:30		6:30		6:30	
7:00		7:00		7:00		7:00	
7:30		7:30		7:30		7:30	
8:00		8:00		8:00		8:00	
8:30		8:30		8:30		8:30	
9:00		9:00		9:00		9:00	
9:30		9:30		9:30		9:30	
10:00		10:00		10:00		10:00	
10:30		10:30		10:30		10:30	
11:00		11:00		11:00		11:00	
11:30		11:30		11:30		11:30	
12:00		12:00		12:00		12:00	
12:30		12:30		12:30		12:30	
1:00		1:00		1:00		1:00	
1:30		1:30		1:30		1:30	
2:00		2:00		2:00		2:00	
2:30		2:30		2:30		2:30	
3:00		3:00		3:00		3:00	
3:30		3:30		3:30		3:30	
4:00		4:00		4:00		4:00	
4:30		4:30		4:30		4:30	
5:00		5:00		5:00		5:00	
5:30		5:30		5:30		5:30	
6:00		6:00		6:00		6:00	
6:30		6:30		6:30		6:30	
7:00		7:00		7:00		7:00	
7:30		7:30		7:30		7:30	
8:00		8:00		8:00		8:00	
8:30		8:30		8:30		8:30	
9:00		9:00		9:00		9:00	
9:30		9:30		9:30		9:30	
10:00		10:00		10:00		10:00	
10:30		10:30		10:30		10:30	
11:00		11:00		11:00		11:00	
( )		( )		( )		( )	

WEEKLY REFLECTION

• •

1) What was my greatest accomplishment this week?

2) Who or what am I grateful for?

3) What activity from this last week took away from my focus and time?

4) What is one thing I can do to be better prepared for this week?

5) What am I looking forward to during the upcoming week?

BRAINSTORM

FINANCIAL CHECKBOX

Questions	Yes	No
Did I remain on budget this week?		
Did I buy what I needed over what I wanted?		
If you got paid this week, did you place 10% of it in your savings?		
Have I taken a percentage (1%-10%) to donate?		
Did I use my credit card wisely this week?		

How can I manage my money more wisely this week?

Week of:	Sunday		Monday		Tuesday	
This Week's Goal	S		S		S	
	A		A		A	
	V		V		V	
	E		E		E	
	R		R		R	
	S		S		S	
Intention for the Day	◆		◆		◆	
Grateful for ...	◆		◆		◆	

	Sunday	Monday	Tuesday
Life is 10% what happens to me and 90% of how I react to it. **–CHARLES SWINDOLL**	5:00	5:00	5:00
	5:30	5:30	5:30
	6:00	6:00	6:00
	6:30	6:30	6:30
	7:00	7:00	7:00
	7:30	7:30	7:30
	8:00	8:00	8:00
	8:30	8:30	8:30
	9:00	9:00	9:00
	9:30	9:30	9:30
TO-DO LIST	10:00	10:00	10:00
Highest Priority	10:30	10:30	10:30
	11:00	11:00	11:00
	11:30	11:30	11:30
	12:00	12:00	12:00
	12:30	12:30	12:30
	1:00	1:00	1:00
Definite Priority	1:30	1:30	1:30
	2:00	2:00	2:00
	2:30	2:30	2:30
	3:00	3:00	3:00
	3:30	3:30	3:30
	4:00	4:00	4:00
Lowest Priority	4:30	4:30	4:30
	5:00	5:00	5:00
	5:30	5:30	5:30
	6:00	6:00	6:00
	6:30	6:30	6:30
	7:00	7:00	7:00
	7:30	7:30	7:30
Habit to Work on This Week	8:00	8:00	8:00
	8:30	8:30	8:30
	9:00	9:00	9:00
	9:30	9:30	9:30
	10:00	10:00	10:00
	10:30	10:30	10:30
	11:00	11:00	11:00

Ready for tomorrow?	( )	( )	( )
ALARM			
CLOTHES/BACKPACK			
GLASS OF WATER			
SAVERS PREP			
BEDTIME AFFIRMATIONS			

Wednesday	Thursday	Friday	Saturday
S	S	S	S
A	A	A	A
V	V	V	V
E	E	E	E
R	R	R	R
S	S	S	S
◆	◆	◆	◆
◆	◆	◆	◆

Wednesday	Thursday	Friday	Saturday
5:00	5:00	5:00	5:00
5:30	5:30	5:30	5:30
6:00	6:00	6:00	6:00
6:30	6:30	6:30	6:30
7:00	7:00	7:00	7:00
7:30	7:30	7:30	7:30
8:00	8:00	8:00	8:00
8:30	8:30	8:30	8:30
9:00	9:00	9:00	9:00
9:30	9:30	9:30	9:30
10:00	10:00	10:00	10:00
10:30	10:30	10:30	10:30
11:00	11:00	11:00	11:00
11:30	11:30	11:30	11:30
12:00	12:00	12:00	12:00
12:30	12:30	12:30	12:30
1:00	1:00	1:00	1:00
1:30	1:30	1:30	1:30
2:00	2:00	2:00	2:00
2:30	2:30	2:30	2:30
3:00	3:00	3:00	3:00
3:30	3:30	3:30	3:30
4:00	4:00	4:00	4:00
4:30	4:30	4:30	4:30
5:00	5:00	5:00	5:00
5:30	5:30	5:30	5:30
6:00	6:00	6:00	6:00
6:30	6:30	6:30	6:30
7:00	7:00	7:00	7:00
7:30	7:30	7:30	7:30
8:00	8:00	8:00	8:00
8:30	8:30	8:30	8:30
9:00	9:00	9:00	9:00
9:30	9:30	9:30	9:30
10:00	10:00	10:00	10:00
10:30	10:30	10:30	10:30
11:00	11:00	11:00	11:00

| ( ) | ( ) | ( ) | ( ) |

WEEKLY REFLECTION

• •

1) What was my greatest accomplishment this week?

2) Who or what am I grateful for?

3) What activity from this last week took away from my focus and time?

4) What is one thing I can do to be better prepared for this week?

5) What am I looking forward to during the upcoming week?

BRAINSTORM

FINANCIAL CHECKBOX

Questions	Yes	No
Did I remain on budget this week?		
Did I buy what I needed over what I wanted?		
If you got paid this week, did you place 10% of it in your savings?		
Have I taken a percentage (1%-10%) to donate?		
Did I use my credit card wisely this week?		

How can I manage my money more wisely this week?

MONTHLY REFLECTION

· ·

Write 5 things you accomplished this month:

1.

2.

3.

4.

5.

QUESTIONS

1) What did I learn about myself this month?

2) What tasks are left over from this month that are lingering and need to get done?

3. Did I take care of myself?

4) What could I have done differently this past month?

5) What areas can I (still) improve on?

6) What experiences can I treasure?

7) What challenged me and how did I overcome the challenge?

8) What specific habits and/or rituals could I develop this month to support my vision?

MONTH OF:	SUNDAY	MONDAY	TUESDAY
This Month's Goal			
Important Events or Reminders to Transfer to My Phone			
1.			
2.			
3.			
4.			
5.			
6.			
7.			
8.			
9.			
10.			

PROJECT NAME	CLASS & INSTRUCTOR	IMPORTANT DATES	DEADLINES
1.			
2.			
3.			
4.			

WEDNESDAY	THURSDAY	FRIDAY	SATURDAY

BRAINSTORM

Week of:		Sunday		Monday		Tuesday	
This Week's Goal		S		S		S	
		A		A		A	
		V		V		V	
		E		E		E	
		R		R		R	
		S		S		S	
Intention for the Day		◆		◆		◆	
Grateful for ...		◆		◆		◆	

The best time to plant a tree was 20 years ago. The second best time is now.

–CHINESE PROVERB

TO-DO LIST
Highest Priority
Definite Priority
Lowest Priority
Habit to Work on This Week

Time	Sunday	Monday	Tuesday
5:00			
5:30			
6:00			
6:30			
7:00			
7:30			
8:00			
8:30			
9:00			
9:30			
10:00			
10:30			
11:00			
11:30			
12:00			
12:30			
1:00			
1:30			
2:00			
2:30			
3:00			
3:30			
4:00			
4:30			
5:00			
5:30			
6:00			
6:30			
7:00			
7:30			
8:00			
8:30			
9:00			
9:30			
10:00			
10:30			
11:00			

Ready for tomorrow?	( )	( )	( )
ALARM			
CLOTHES/BACKPACK			
GLASS OF WATER			
SAVERS PREP			
BEDTIME AFFIRMATIONS			

Wednesday		Thursday		Friday		Saturday	
S		S		S		S	
A		A		A		A	
V		V		V		V	
E		E		E		E	
R		R		R		R	
S		S		S		S	
◆		◆		◆		◆	
◆		◆		◆		◆	

Wednesday		Thursday		Friday		Saturday	
5:00		5:00		5:00		5:00	
5:30		5:30		5:30		5:30	
6:00		6:00		6:00		6:00	
6:30		6:30		6:30		6:30	
7:00		7:00		7:00		7:00	
7:30		7:30		7:30		7:30	
8:00		8:00		8:00		8:00	
8:30		8:30		8:30		8:30	
9:00		9:00		9:00		9:00	
9:30		9:30		9:30		9:30	
10:00		10:00		10:00		10:00	
10:30		10:30		10:30		10:30	
11:00		11:00		11:00		11:00	
11:30		11:30		11:30		11:30	
12:00		12:00		12:00		12:00	
12:30		12:30		12:30		12:30	
1:00		1:00		1:00		1:00	
1:30		1:30		1:30		1:30	
2:00		2:00		2:00		2:00	
2:30		2:30		2:30		2:30	
3:00		3:00		3:00		3:00	
3:30		3:30		3:30		3:30	
4:00		4:00		4:00		4:00	
4:30		4:30		4:30		4:30	
5:00		5:00		5:00		5:00	
5:30		5:30		5:30		5:30	
6:00		6:00		6:00		6:00	
6:30		6:30		6:30		6:30	
7:00		7:00		7:00		7:00	
7:30		7:30		7:30		7:30	
8:00		8:00		8:00		8:00	
8:30		8:30		8:30		8:30	
9:00		9:00		9:00		9:00	
9:30		9:30		9:30		9:30	
10:00		10:00		10:00		10:00	
10:30		10:30		10:30		10:30	
11:00		11:00		11:00		11:00	
	( )		( )		( )		( )

WEEKLY REFLECTION

• •

1) What was my greatest accomplishment this week?

2) Who or what am I grateful for?

3) What activity from this last week took away from my focus and time?

4) What is one thing I can do to be better prepared for this week?

5) What am I looking forward to during the upcoming week?

BRAINSTORM

FINANCIAL CHECKBOX

Questions	Yes	No
Did I remain on budget this week?		
Did I buy what I needed over what I wanted?		
If you got paid this week, did you place 10% of it in your savings?		
Have I taken a percentage (1%-10%) to donate?		
Did I use my credit card wisely this week?		

How can I manage my money more wisely this week?

Week of:	Sunday	Monday	Tuesday
This Week's Goal	S	S	S
	A	A	A
	V	V	V
	E	E	E
	R	R	R
	S	S	S
Intention for the Day	◆	◆	◆
Grateful for ...	◆	◆	◆

I've learned that people will forget what you said, people will forget what you did, but people will never forget how you made them feel.

—MAYA ANGELOU

TO-DO LIST
Highest Priority
Definite Priority
Lowest Priority
Habit to Work on This Week

Sunday	Monday	Tuesday
5:00	5:00	5:00
5:30	5:30	5:30
6:00	6:00	6:00
6:30	6:30	6:30
7:00	7:00	7:00
7:30	7:30	7:30
8:00	8:00	8:00
8:30	8:30	8:30
9:00	9:00	9:00
9:30	9:30	9:30
10:00	10:00	10:00
10:30	10:30	10:30
11:00	11:00	11:00
11:30	11:30	11:30
12:00	12:00	12:00
12:30	12:30	12:30
1:00	1:00	1:00
1:30	1:30	1:30
2:00	2:00	2:00
2:30	2:30	2:30
3:00	3:00	3:00
3:30	3:30	3:30
4:00	4:00	4:00
4:30	4:30	4:30
5:00	5:00	5:00
5:30	5:30	5:30
6:00	6:00	6:00
6:30	6:30	6:30
7:00	7:00	7:00
7:30	7:30	7:30
8:00	8:00	8:00
8:30	8:30	8:30
9:00	9:00	9:00
9:30	9:30	9:30
10:00	10:00	10:00
10:30	10:30	10:30
11:00	11:00	11:00

Ready for tomorrow?	( )	( )	( )
ALARM			
CLOTHES/BACKPACK			
GLASS OF WATER			
SAVERS PREP			
BEDTIME AFFIRMATIONS			

Wednesday		Thursday		Friday		Saturday	
S		S		S		S	
A		A		A		A	
V		V		V		V	
E		E		E		E	
R		R		R		R	
S		S		S		S	
◆		◆		◆		◆	
◆		◆		◆		◆	
5:00		5:00		5:00		5:00	
5:30		5:30		5:30		5:30	
6:00		6:00		6:00		6:00	
6:30		6:30		6:30		6:30	
7:00		7:00		7:00		7:00	
7:30		7:30		7:30		7:30	
8:00		8:00		8:00		8:00	
8:30		8:30		8:30		8:30	
9:00		9:00		9:00		9:00	
9:30		9:30		9:30		9:30	
10:00		10:00		10:00		10:00	
10:30		10:30		10:30		10:30	
11:00		11:00		11:00		11:00	
11:30		11:30		11:30		11:30	
12:00		12:00		12:00		12:00	
12:30		12:30		12:30		12:30	
1:00		1:00		1:00		1:00	
1:30		1:30		1:30		1:30	
2:00		2:00		2:00		2:00	
2:30		2:30		2:30		2:30	
3:00		3:00		3:00		3:00	
3:30		3:30		3:30		3:30	
4:00		4:00		4:00		4:00	
4:30		4:30		4:30		4:30	
5:00		5:00		5:00		5:00	
5:30		5:30		5:30		5:30	
6:00		6:00		6:00		6:00	
6:30		6:30		6:30		6:30	
7:00		7:00		7:00		7:00	
7:30		7:30		7:30		7:30	
8:00		8:00		8:00		8:00	
8:30		8:30		8:30		8:30	
9:00		9:00		9:00		9:00	
9:30		9:30		9:30		9:30	
10:00		10:00		10:00		10:00	
10:30		10:30		10:30		10:30	
11:00		11:00		11:00		11:00	
( )		( )		( )		( )	

WEEKLY REFLECTION

••

1) What was my greatest accomplishment this week?

2) Who or what am I grateful for?

3) What activity from this last week took away from my focus and time?

4) What is one thing I can do to be better prepared for this week?

5) What am I looking forward to during the upcoming week?

BRAINSTORM

FINANCIAL CHECKBOX

Questions	Yes	No
Did I remain on budget this week?		
Did I buy what I needed over what I wanted?		
If you got paid this week, did you place 10% of it in your savings?		
Have I taken a percentage (1%-10%) to donate?		
Did I use my credit card wisely this week?		

How can I manage my money more wisely this week?

Week of:	Sunday	Monday	Tuesday
This Week's Goal	S	S	S
	A	A	A
	V	V	V
	E	E	E
	R	R	R
	S	S	S
Intention for the Day	◆	◆	◆
Grateful for ...	◆	◆	◆

Nothing will prove to be your greatest teacher more than your failures. So keep trying, keep succeeding, and keep failing. There is something to learn in all those experiences.

—NATALIE JANJI

TO-DO LIST
Highest Priority
Definite Priority
Lowest Priority
Habit to Work on This Week

Time (Sunday)	Time (Monday)	Time (Tuesday)
5:00	5:00	5:00
5:30	5:30	5:30
6:00	6:00	6:00
6:30	6:30	6:30
7:00	7:00	7:00
7:30	7:30	7:30
8:00	8:00	8:00
8:30	8:30	8:30
9:00	9:00	9:00
9:30	9:30	9:30
10:00	10:00	10:00
10:30	10:30	10:30
11:00	11:00	11:00
11:30	11:30	11:30
12:00	12:00	12:00
12:30	12:30	12:30
1:00	1:00	1:00
1:30	1:30	1:30
2:00	2:00	2:00
2:30	2:30	2:30
3:00	3:00	3:00
3:30	3:30	3:30
4:00	4:00	4:00
4:30	4:30	4:30
5:00	5:00	5:00
5:30	5:30	5:30
6:00	6:00	6:00
6:30	6:30	6:30
7:00	7:00	7:00
7:30	7:30	7:30
8:00	8:00	8:00
8:30	8:30	8:30
9:00	9:00	9:00
9:30	9:30	9:30
10:00	10:00	10:00
10:30	10:30	10:30
11:00	11:00	11:00

Ready for tomorrow?	( )	( )	( )
ALARM			
CLOTHES/BACKPACK			
GLASS OF WATER			
SAVERS PREP			
BEDTIME AFFIRMATIONS			

Wednesday	Thursday	Friday	Saturday
S	S	S	S
A	A	A	A
V	V	V	V
E	E	E	E
R	R	R	R
S	S	S	S
◆	◆	◆	◆
◆	◆	◆	◆

Wednesday	Thursday	Friday	Saturday
5:00	5:00	5:00	5:00
5:30	5:30	5:30	5:30
6:00	6:00	6:00	6:00
6:30	6:30	6:30	6:30
7:00	7:00	7:00	7:00
7:30	7:30	7:30	7:30
8:00	8:00	8:00	8:00
8:30	8:30	8:30	8:30
9:00	9:00	9:00	9:00
9:30	9:30	9:30	9:30
10:00	10:00	10:00	10:00
10:30	10:30	10:30	10:30
11:00	11:00	11:00	11:00
11:30	11:30	11:30	11:30
12:00	12:00	12:00	12:00
12:30	12:30	12:30	12:30
1:00	1:00	1:00	1:00
1:30	1:30	1:30	1:30
2:00	2:00	2:00	2:00
2:30	2:30	2:30	2:30
3:00	3:00	3:00	3:00
3:30	3:30	3:30	3:30
4:00	4:00	4:00	4:00
4:30	4:30	4:30	4:30
5:00	5:00	5:00	5:00
5:30	5:30	5:30	5:30
6:00	6:00	6:00	6:00
6:30	6:30	6:30	6:30
7:00	7:00	7:00	7:00
7:30	7:30	7:30	7:30
8:00	8:00	8:00	8:00
8:30	8:30	8:30	8:30
9:00	9:00	9:00	9:00
9:30	9:30	9:30	9:30
10:00	10:00	10:00	10:00
10:30	10:30	10:30	10:30
11:00	11:00	11:00	11:00
( )	( )	( )	( )

WEEKLY REFLECTION

• •

1) What was my greatest accomplishment this week?

2) Who or what am I grateful for?

3) What activity from this last week took away from my focus and time?

4) What is one thing I can do to be better prepared for this week?

5) What am I looking forward to during the upcoming week?

BRAINSTORM

FINANCIAL CHECKBOX

Questions	Yes	No
Did I remain on budget this week?		
Did I buy what I needed over what I wanted?		
If you got paid this week, did you place 10% of it in your savings?		
Have I taken a percentage (1%-10%) to donate?		
Did I use my credit card wisely this week?		
How can I manage my money more wisely this week?		

Week of:	Sunday	Monday	Tuesday
This Week's Goal	S	S	S
	A	A	A
	V	V	V
	E	E	E
	R	R	R
	S	S	S
Intention for the Day	◆	◆	◆
Grateful for ...	◆	◆	◆

	Sunday	Monday	Tuesday
Whatever you think is possible is possible with the right plan and the right actions. —**HONORÉE CORDER**	5:00	5:00	5:00
	5:30	5:30	5:30
	6:00	6:00	6:00
	6:30	6:30	6:30
	7:00	7:00	7:00
	7:30	7:30	7:30
	8:00	8:00	8:00
	8:30	8:30	8:30
	9:00	9:00	9:00
	9:30	9:30	9:30
TO-DO LIST	10:00	10:00	10:00
Highest Priority	10:30	10:30	10:30
	11:00	11:00	11:00
	11:30	11:30	11:30
	12:00	12:00	12:00
	12:30	12:30	12:30
	1:00	1:00	1:00
Definite Priority	1:30	1:30	1:30
	2:00	2:00	2:00
	2:30	2:30	2:30
	3:00	3:00	3:00
	3:30	3:30	3:30
	4:00	4:00	4:00
Lowest Priority	4:30	4:30	4:30
	5:00	5:00	5:00
	5:30	5:30	5:30
	6:00	6:00	6:00
	6:30	6:30	6:30
	7:00	7:00	7:00
	7:30	7:30	7:30
Habit to Work on This Week	8:00	8:00	8:00
	8:30	8:30	8:30
	9:00	9:00	9:00
	9:30	9:30	9:30
	10:00	10:00	10:00
	10:30	10:30	10:30
	11:00	11:00	11:00

Ready for tomorrow?	( )	( )	( )
ALARM			
CLOTHES/BACKPACK			
GLASS OF WATER			
SAVERS PREP			
BEDTIME AFFIRMATIONS			

Wednesday	Thursday	Friday	Saturday
S	S	S	S
A	A	A	A
V	V	V	V
E	E	E	E
R	R	R	R
S	S	S	S
◆	◆	◆	◆
◆	◆	◆	◆

Wednesday	Thursday	Friday	Saturday
5:00	5:00	5:00	5:00
5:30	5:30	5:30	5:30
6:00	6:00	6:00	6:00
6:30	6:30	6:30	6:30
7:00	7:00	7:00	7:00
7:30	7:30	7:30	7:30
8:00	8:00	8:00	8:00
8:30	8:30	8:30	8:30
9:00	9:00	9:00	9:00
9:30	9:30	9:30	9:30
10:00	10:00	10:00	10:00
10:30	10:30	10:30	10:30
11:00	11:00	11:00	11:00
11:30	11:30	11:30	11:30
12:00	12:00	12:00	12:00
12:30	12:30	12:30	12:30
1:00	1:00	1:00	1:00
1:30	1:30	1:30	1:30
2:00	2:00	2:00	2:00
2:30	2:30	2:30	2:30
3:00	3:00	3:00	3:00
3:30	3:30	3:30	3:30
4:00	4:00	4:00	4:00
4:30	4:30	4:30	4:30
5:00	5:00	5:00	5:00
5:30	5:30	5:30	5:30
6:00	6:00	6:00	6:00
6:30	6:30	6:30	6:30
7:00	7:00	7:00	7:00
7:30	7:30	7:30	7:30
8:00	8:00	8:00	8:00
8:30	8:30	8:30	8:30
9:00	9:00	9:00	9:00
9:30	9:30	9:30	9:30
10:00	10:00	10:00	10:00
10:30	10:30	10:30	10:30
11:00	11:00	11:00	11:00

( )	( )	( )	( )

WEEKLY REFLECTION

· ·

1) What was my greatest accomplishment this week?

2) Who or what am I grateful for?

3) What activity from this last week took away from my focus and time?

4) What is one thing I can do to be better prepared for this week?

5) What am I looking forward to during the upcoming week?

BRAINSTORM

FINANCIAL CHECKBOX

Questions	Yes	No
Did I remain on budget this week?		
Did I buy what I needed over what I wanted?		
If you got paid this week, did you place 10% of it in your savings?		
Have I taken a percentage (1%-10%) to donate?		
Did I use my credit card wisely this week?		
How can I manage my money more wisely this week?		

Week of:	Sunday		Monday		Tuesday	
This Week's Goal	S		S		S	
	A		A		A	
	V		V		V	
	E		E		E	
	R		R		R	
	S		S		S	
Intention for the Day	◆		◆		◆	
Grateful for …	◆		◆		◆	

> *How wonderful it is that nobody need wait a single moment before starting to improve the world.*
>
> —ANNE FRANK

	Sunday	Monday	Tuesday
	5:00	5:00	5:00
	5:30	5:30	5:30
	6:00	6:00	6:00
	6:30	6:30	6:30
	7:00	7:00	7:00
	7:30	7:30	7:30
	8:00	8:00	8:00
	8:30	8:30	8:30
	9:00	9:00	9:00
	9:30	9:30	9:30
TO-DO LIST	10:00	10:00	10:00
Highest Priority	10:30	10:30	10:30
	11:00	11:00	11:00
	11:30	11:30	11:30
	12:00	12:00	12:00
	12:30	12:30	12:30
	1:00	1:00	1:00
Definite Priority	1:30	1:30	1:30
	2:00	2:00	2:00
	2:30	2:30	2:30
	3:00	3:00	3:00
	3:30	3:30	3:30
	4:00	4:00	4:00
Lowest Priority	4:30	4:30	4:30
	5:00	5:00	5:00
	5:30	5:30	5:30
	6:00	6:00	6:00
	6:30	6:30	6:30
	7:00	7:00	7:00
	7:30	7:30	7:30
Habit to Work on This Week	8:00	8:00	8:00
	8:30	8:30	8:30
	9:00	9:00	9:00
	9:30	9:30	9:30
	10:00	10:00	10:00
	10:30	10:30	10:30
	11:00	11:00	11:00

Ready for tomorrow?	( )	( )	( )
ALARM			
CLOTHES/BACKPACK			
GLASS OF WATER			
SAVERS PREP			
BEDTIME AFFIRMATIONS			

Wednesday	Thursday	Friday	Saturday
S	S	S	S
A	A	A	A
V	V	V	V
E	E	E	E
R	R	R	R
S	S	S	S
◆	◆	◆	◆
◆	◆	◆	◆

Wednesday		Thursday		Friday		Saturday	
5:00		5:00		5:00		5:00	
5:30		5:30		5:30		5:30	
6:00		6:00		6:00		6:00	
6:30		6:30		6:30		6:30	
7:00		7:00		7:00		7:00	
7:30		7:30		7:30		7:30	
8:00		8:00		8:00		8:00	
8:30		8:30		8:30		8:30	
9:00		9:00		9:00		9:00	
9:30		9:30		9:30		9:30	
10:00		10:00		10:00		10:00	
10:30		10:30		10:30		10:30	
11:00		11:00		11:00		11:00	
11:30		11:30		11:30		11:30	
12:00		12:00		12:00		12:00	
12:30		12:30		12:30		12:30	
1:00		1:00		1:00		1:00	
1:30		1:30		1:30		1:30	
2:00		2:00		2:00		2:00	
2:30		2:30		2:30		2:30	
3:00		3:00		3:00		3:00	
3:30		3:30		3:30		3:30	
4:00		4:00		4:00		4:00	
4:30		4:30		4:30		4:30	
5:00		5:00		5:00		5:00	
5:30		5:30		5:30		5:30	
6:00		6:00		6:00		6:00	
6:30		6:30		6:30		6:30	
7:00		7:00		7:00		7:00	
7:30		7:30		7:30		7:30	
8:00		8:00		8:00		8:00	
8:30		8:30		8:30		8:30	
9:00		9:00		9:00		9:00	
9:30		9:30		9:30		9:30	
10:00		10:00		10:00		10:00	
10:30		10:30		10:30		10:30	
11:00		11:00		11:00			

( )	( )	( )	( )

WEEKLY REFLECTION

....

1) What was my greatest accomplishment this week?

2) Who or what am I grateful for?

3) What activity from this last week took away from my focus and time?

4) What is one thing I can do to be better prepared for this week?

5) What am I looking forward to during the upcoming week?

BRAINSTORM

FINANCIAL CHECKBOX

Questions	Yes	No
Did I remain on budget this week?		
Did I buy what I needed over what I wanted?		
If you got paid this week, did you place 10% of it in your savings?		
Have I taken a percentage (1%-10%) to donate?		
Did I use my credit card wisely this week?		
How can I manage my money more wisely this week?		

MONTHLY REFLECTION

· ·

Write 5 things you accomplished this month:

1.

2.

3.

4.

5.

QUESTIONS

1) What did I learn about myself this month?

2) What tasks are left over from this month that are lingering and need to get done?

3. Did I take care of myself?

4) What could I have done differently this past month?

5) What areas can I (still) improve on?

6) What experiences can I treasure?

7) What challenged me and how did I overcome the challenge?

8) What specific habits and/or rituals could I develop this month to support my vision?

MONTH OF:	SUNDAY	MONDAY	TUESDAY
This Month's Goal			
Important Events or Reminders to Transfer to My Phone			
1.			
2.			
3.			
4.			
5.			
6.			
7.			
8.			
9.			
10.			

PROJECT NAME	CLASS & INSTRUCTOR	IMPORTANT DATES	DEADLINES
1.			
2.			
3.			
4.			

WEDNESDAY	THURSDAY	FRIDAY	SATURDAY

BRAINSTORM

Week of:	Sunday	Monday	Tuesday	
This Week's Goal	S	S	S	
	A	A	A	
	V	V	V	
	E	E	E	
	R	R	R	
	S	S	S	
Intention for the Day	◆	◆	◆	
Grateful for ...	◆	◆	◆	

Success is going from failure to failure without losing your enthusiasm.

–WINSTON CHURCHILL

TO-DO LIST				
Highest Priority				

	Sunday	Monday	Tuesday
5:00		5:00	5:00
5:30		5:30	5:30
6:00		6:00	6:00
6:30		6:30	6:30
7:00		7:00	7:00
7:30		7:30	7:30
8:00		8:00	8:00
8:30		8:30	8:30
9:00		9:00	9:00
9:30		9:30	9:30
10:00		10:00	10:00
10:30		10:30	10:30
11:00		11:00	11:00
11:30		11:30	11:30
12:00		12:00	12:00
12:30		12:30	12:30
1:00		1:00	1:00
1:30		1:30	1:30
2:00		2:00	2:00
2:30		2:30	2:30
3:00		3:00	3:00
3:30		3:30	3:30
4:00		4:00	4:00
4:30		4:30	4:30
5:00		5:00	5:00
5:30		5:30	5:30
6:00		6:00	6:00
6:30		6:30	6:30
7:00		7:00	7:00
7:30		7:30	7:30
8:00		8:00	8:00
8:30		8:30	8:30
9:00		9:00	9:00
9:30		9:30	9:30
10:00		10:00	10:00
10:30		10:30	10:30
11:00		11:00	11:00

To-do list side labels:
- Definite Priority
- Lowest Priority
- Habit to Work on This Week

Ready for tomorrow?	( )	( )	( )
ALARM			
CLOTHES/BACKPACK			
GLASS OF WATER			
SAVERS PREP			
BEDTIME AFFIRMATIONS			

Wednesday		Thursday		Friday		Saturday	
S		S		S		S	
A		A		A		A	
V		V		V		V	
E		E		E		E	
R		R		R		R	
S		S		S		S	
◆		◆		◆		◆	
◆		◆		◆		◆	
5:00		5:00		5:00		5:00	
5:30		5:30		5:30		5:30	
6:00		6:00		6:00		6:00	
6:30		6:30		6:30		6:30	
7:00		7:00		7:00		7:00	
7:30		7:30		7:30		7:30	
8:00		8:00		8:00		8:00	
8:30		8:30		8:30		8:30	
9:00		9:00		9:00		9:00	
9:30		9:30		9:30		9:30	
10:00		10:00		10:00		10:00	
10:30		10:30		10:30		10:30	
11:00		11:00		11:00		11:00	
11:30		11:30		11:30		11:30	
12:00		12:00		12:00		12:00	
12:30		12:30		12:30		12:30	
1:00		1:00		1:00		1:00	
1:30		1:30		1:30		1:30	
2:00		2:00		2:00		2:00	
2:30		2:30		2:30		2:30	
3:00		3:00		3:00		3:00	
3:30		3:30		3:30		3:30	
4:00		4:00		4:00		4:00	
4:30		4:30		4:30		4:30	
5:00		5:00		5:00		5:00	
5:30		5:30		5:30		5:30	
6:00		6:00		6:00		6:00	
6:30		6:30		6:30		6:30	
7:00		7:00		7:00		7:00	
7:30		7:30		7:30		7:30	
8:00		8:00		8:00		8:00	
8:30		8:30		8:30		8:30	
9:00		9:00		9:00		9:00	
9:30		9:30		9:30		9:30	
10:00		10:00		10:00		10:00	
10:30		10:30		10:30		10:30	
11:00		11:00		11:00		11:00	
( )		( )		( )		( )	

WEEKLY REFLECTION

• •

1) What was my greatest accomplishment this week?

2) Who or what am I grateful for?

3) What activity from this last week took away from my focus and time?

4) What is one thing I can do to be better prepared for this week?

5) What am I looking forward to during the upcoming week?

BRAINSTORM

FINANCIAL CHECKBOX

Questions	Yes	No
Did I remain on budget this week?		
Did I buy what I needed over what I wanted?		
If you got paid this week, did you place 10% of it in your savings?		
Have I taken a percentage (1%-10%) to donate?		
Did I use my credit card wisely this week?		

How can I manage my money more wisely this week?

Week of:	Sunday	Monday	Tuesday
This Week's Goal	S	S	S
	A	A	A
	V	V	V
	E	E	E
	R	R	R
	S	S	S
Intention for the Day	◆	◆	◆
Grateful for ...	◆	◆	◆

Dream big and dare to fail.

–NORMAN VAUGHAN

TO-DO LIST

Highest Priority

Definite Priority

Lowest Priority

Habit to Work on This Week

	Sunday	Monday	Tuesday
5:00		5:00		5:00	
5:30		5:30		5:30	
6:00		6:00		6:00	
6:30		6:30		6:30	
7:00		7:00		7:00	
7:30		7:30		7:30	
8:00		8:00		8:00	
8:30		8:30		8:30	
9:00		9:00		9:00	
9:30		9:30		9:30	
10:00		10:00		10:00	
10:30		10:30		10:30	
11:00		11:00		11:00	
11:30		11:30		11:30	
12:00		12:00		12:00	
12:30		12:30		12:30	
1:00		1:00		1:00	
1:30		1:30		1:30	
2:00		2:00		2:00	
2:30		2:30		2:30	
3:00		3:00		3:00	
3:30		3:30		3:30	
4:00		4:00		4:00	
4:30		4:30		4:30	
5:00		5:00		5:00	
5:30		5:30		5:30	
6:00		6:00		6:00	
6:30		6:30		6:30	
7:00		7:00		7:00	
7:30		7:30		7:30	
8:00		8:00		8:00	
8:30		8:30		8:30	
9:00		9:00		9:00	
9:30		9:30		9:30	
10:00		10:00		10:00	
10:30		10:30		10:30	
11:00		11:00		11:00	

Ready for tomorrow?	( )	( )	( )
ALARM			
CLOTHES/BACKPACK			
GLASS OF WATER			
SAVERS PREP			
BEDTIME AFFIRMATIONS			

Wednesday		Thursday		Friday		Saturday	
S		S		S		S	
A		A		A		A	
V		V		V		V	
E		E		E		E	
R		R		R		R	
S		S		S		S	
◆		◆		◆		◆	
◆		◆		◆		◆	

Wednesday	Thursday	Friday	Saturday
5:00	5:00	5:00	5:00
5:30	5:30	5:30	5:30
6:00	6:00	6:00	6:00
6:30	6:30	6:30	6:30
7:00	7:00	7:00	7:00
7:30	7:30	7:30	7:30
8:00	8:00	8:00	8:00
8:30	8:30	8:30	8:30
9:00	9:00	9:00	9:00
9:30	9:30	9:30	9:30
10:00	10:00	10:00	10:00
10:30	10:30	10:30	10:30
11:00	11:00	11:00	11:00
11:30	11:30	11:30	11:30
12:00	12:00	12:00	12:00
12:30	12:30	12:30	12:30
1:00	1:00	1:00	1:00
1:30	1:30	1:30	1:30
2:00	2:00	2:00	2:00
2:30	2:30	2:30	2:30
3:00	3:00	3:00	3:00
3:30	3:30	3:30	3:30
4:00	4:00	4:00	4:00
4:30	4:30	4:30	4:30
5:00	5:00	5:00	5:00
5:30	5:30	5:30	5:30
6:00	6:00	6:00	6:00
6:30	6:30	6:30	6:30
7:00	7:00	7:00	7:00
7:30	7:30	7:30	7:30
8:00	8:00	8:00	8:00
8:30	8:30	8:30	8:30
9:00	9:00	9:00	9:00
9:30	9:30	9:30	9:30
10:00	10:00	10:00	10:00
10:30	10:30	10:30	10:30
11:00	11:00	11:00	11:00

( )	( )	( )	( )

WEEKLY REFLECTION

. . . .

1) What was my greatest accomplishment this week?

2) Who or what am I grateful for?

3) What activity from this last week took away from my focus and time?

4) What is one thing I can do to be better prepared for this week?

5) What am I looking forward to during the upcoming week?

BRAINSTORM

FINANCIAL CHECKBOX

Questions	Yes	No
Did I remain on budget this week?		
Did I buy what I needed over what I wanted?		
If you got paid this week, did you place 10% of it in your savings?		
Have I taken a percentage (1%-10%) to donate?		
Did I use my credit card wisely this week?		
How can I manage my money more wisely this week?		

Week of:		Sunday		Monday		Tuesday	
This Week's Goal		S		S		S	
		A		A		A	
		V		V		V	
		E		E		E	
		R		R		R	
		S		S		S	
Intention for the Day		◆		◆		◆	
Grateful for ...		◆		◆		◆	

You must be the change you wish to see in the world.

—GANDHI

TO-DO LIST

Highest Priority

Definite Priority

Lowest Priority

Habit to Work on This Week

Time	Sunday	Monday	Tuesday
5:00			
5:30			
6:00			
6:30			
7:00			
7:30			
8:00			
8:30			
9:00			
9:30			
10:00			
10:30			
11:00			
11:30			
12:00			
12:30			
1:00			
1:30			
2:00			
2:30			
3:00			
3:30			
4:00			
4:30			
5:00			
5:30			
6:00			
6:30			
7:00			
7:30			
8:00			
8:30			
9:00			
9:30			
10:00			
10:30			
11:00			

Ready for tomorrow?		( )		( )		( )
ALARM						
CLOTHES/BACKPACK						
GLASS OF WATER						
SAVERS PREP						
BEDTIME AFFIRMATIONS						

Wednesday		Thursday		Friday		Saturday	
S		S		S		S	
A		A		A		A	
V		V		V		V	
E		E		E		E	
R		R		R		R	
S		S		S		S	
◆		◆		◆		◆	
◆		◆		◆		◆	
5:00		5:00		5:00		5:00	
5:30		5:30		5:30		5:30	
6:00		6:00		6:00		6:00	
6:30		6:30		6:30		6:30	
7:00		7:00		7:00		7:00	
7:30		7:30		7:30		7:30	
8:00		8:00		8:00		8:00	
8:30		8:30		8:30		8:30	
9:00		9:00		9:00		9:00	
9:30		9:30		9:30		9:30	
10:00		10:00		10:00		10:00	
10:30		10:30		10:30		10:30	
11:00		11:00		11:00		11:00	
11:30		11:30		11:30		11:30	
12:00		12:00		12:00		12:00	
12:30		12:30		12:30		12:30	
1:00		1:00		1:00		1:00	
1:30		1:30		1:30		1:30	
2:00		2:00		2:00		2:00	
2:30		2:30		2:30		2:30	
3:00		3:00		3:00		3:00	
3:30		3:30		3:30		3:30	
4:00		4:00		4:00		4:00	
4:30		4:30		4:30		4:30	
5:00		5:00		5:00		5:00	
5:30		5:30		5:30		5:30	
6:00		6:00		6:00		6:00	
6:30		6:30		6:30		6:30	
7:00		7:00		7:00		7:00	
7:30		7:30		7:30		7:30	
8:00		8:00		8:00		8:00	
8:30		8:30		8:30		8:30	
9:00		9:00		9:00		9:00	
9:30		9:30		9:30		9:30	
10:00		10:00		10:00		10:00	
10:30		10:30		10:30		10:30	
11:00		11:00		11:00		11:00	
	( )		( )		( )		( )

WEEKLY REFLECTION

• •

1) What was my greatest accomplishment this week?

2) Who or what am I grateful for?

3) What activity from this last week took away from my focus and time?

4) What is one thing I can do to be better prepared for this week?

5) What am I looking forward to during the upcoming week?

BRAINSTORM

FINANCIAL CHECKBOX

Questions	Yes	No
Did I remain on budget this week?		
Did I buy what I needed over what I wanted?		
If you got paid this week, did you place 10% of it in your savings?		
Have I taken a percentage (1%-10%) to donate?		
Did I use my credit card wisely this week?		

How can I manage my money more wisely this week?

Week of:	Sunday		Monday		Tuesday	
This Week's Goal	S		S		S	
	A		A		A	
	V		V		V	
	E		E		E	
	R		R		R	
	S		S		S	
Intention for the Day	◆		◆		◆	
Grateful for ...	◆		◆		◆	

	Sunday	Monday	Tuesday
Keep your face to the sunshine and you can never see the shadow. —**HELEN KELLER**	5:00	5:00	5:00
	5:30	5:30	5:30
	6:00	6:00	6:00
	6:30	6:30	6:30
	7:00	7:00	7:00
	7:30	7:30	7:30
	8:00	8:00	8:00
	8:30	8:30	8:30
	9:00	9:00	9:00
	9:30	9:30	9:30
TO-DO LIST	10:00	10:00	10:00
Highest Priority	10:30	10:30	10:30
	11:00	11:00	11:00
	11:30	11:30	11:30
	12:00	12:00	12:00
	12:30	12:30	12:30
	1:00	1:00	1:00
Definite Priority	1:30	1:30	1:30
	2:00	2:00	2:00
	2:30	2:30	2:30
	3:00	3:00	3:00
	3:30	3:30	3:30
	4:00	4:00	4:00
Lowest Priority	4:30	4:30	4:30
	5:00	5:00	5:00
	5:30	5:30	5:30
	6:00	6:00	6:00
	6:30	6:30	6:30
	7:00	7:00	7:00
	7:30	7:30	7:30
Habit to Work on This Week	8:00	8:00	8:00
	8:30	8:30	8:30
	9:00	9:00	9:00
	9:30	9:30	9:30
	10:00	10:00	10:00
	10:30	10:30	10:30
	11:00	11:00	11:00

Ready for tomorrow?	( )	( )	( )
ALARM			
CLOTHES/BACKPACK			
GLASS OF WATER			
SAVERS PREP			
BEDTIME AFFIRMATIONS			

Wednesday		Thursday		Friday		Saturday	
S		S		S		S	
A		A		A		A	
V		V		V		V	
E		E		E		E	
R		R		R		R	
S		S		S		S	
◆		◆		◆		◆	
◆		◆		◆		◆	
5:00		5:00		5:00		5:00	
5:30		5:30		5:30		5:30	
6:00		6:00		6:00		6:00	
6:30		6:30		6:30		6:30	
7:00		7:00		7:00		7:00	
7:30		7:30		7:30		7:30	
8:00		8:00		8:00		8:00	
8:30		8:30		8:30		8:30	
9:00		9:00		9:00		9:00	
9:30		9:30		9:30		9:30	
10:00		10:00		10:00		10:00	
10:30		10:30		10:30		10:30	
11:00		11:00		11:00		11:00	
11:30		11:30		11:30		11:30	
12:00		12:00		12:00		12:00	
12:30		12:30		12:30		12:30	
1:00		1:00		1:00		1:00	
1:30		1:30		1:30		1:30	
2:00		2:00		2:00		2:00	
2:30		2:30		2:30		2:30	
3:00		3:00		3:00		3:00	
3:30		3:30		3:30		3:30	
4:00		4:00		4:00		4:00	
4:30		4:30		4:30		4:30	
5:00		5:00		5:00		5:00	
5:30		5:30		5:30		5:30	
6:00		6:00		6:00		6:00	
6:30		6:30		6:30		6:30	
7:00		7:00		7:00		7:00	
7:30		7:30		7:30		7:30	
8:00		8:00		8:00		8:00	
8:30		8:30		8:30		8:30	
9:00		9:00		9:00		9:00	
9:30		9:30		9:30		9:30	
10:00		10:00		10:00		10:00	
10:30		10:30		10:30		10:30	
11:00		11:00		11:00		11:00	
	( )		( )		( )		( )

WEEKLY REFLECTION

• •

1) What was my greatest accomplishment this week?

2) Who or what am I grateful for?

3) What activity from this last week took away from my focus and time?

4) What is one thing I can do to be better prepared for this week?

5) What am I looking forward to during the upcoming week?

BRAINSTORM

FINANCIAL CHECKBOX

Questions	Yes	No
Did I remain on budget this week?		
Did I buy what I needed over what I wanted?		
If you got paid this week, did you place 10% of it in your savings?		
Have I taken a percentage (1%-10%) to donate?		
Did I use my credit card wisely this week?		

How can I manage my money more wisely this week?

Week of:	Sunday		Monday		Tuesday	
This Week's Goal	S		S		S	
	A		A		A	
	V		V		V	
	E		E		E	
	R		R		R	
	S		S		S	
Intention for the Day	◆		◆		◆	
Grateful for ...	◆		◆		◆	

Every strike brings me closer to the next home run.

—BABE RUTH

TO-DO LIST

Highest Priority

Definite Priority

Lowest Priority

Habit to Work on This Week

Time	Sunday	Monday	Tuesday
5:00			
5:30			
6:00			
6:30			
7:00			
7:30			
8:00			
8:30			
9:00			
9:30			
10:00			
10:30			
11:00			
11:30			
12:00			
12:30			
1:00			
1:30			
2:00			
2:30			
3:00			
3:30			
4:00			
4:30			
5:00			
5:30			
6:00			
6:30			
7:00			
7:30			
8:00			
8:30			
9:00			
9:30			
10:00			
10:30			
11:00			

Ready for tomorrow?	( )	( )	( )
ALARM			
CLOTHES/BACKPACK			
GLASS OF WATER			
SAVERS PREP			
BEDTIME AFFIRMATIONS			

Wednesday	Thursday	Friday	Saturday
S	S	S	S
A	A	A	A
V	V	V	V
E	E	E	E
R	R	R	R
S	S	S	S
◆	◆	◆	◆
◆	◆	◆	◆

Wednesday	Thursday	Friday	Saturday
5:00	5:00	5:00	5:00
5:30	5:30	5:30	5:30
6:00	6:00	6:00	6:00
6:30	6:30	6:30	6:30
7:00	7:00	7:00	7:00
7:30	7:30	7:30	7:30
8:00	8:00	8:00	8:00
8:30	8:30	8:30	8:30
9:00	9:00	9:00	9:00
9:30	9:30	9:30	9:30
10:00	10:00	10:00	10:00
10:30	10:30	10:30	10:30
11:00	11:00	11:00	11:00
11:30	11:30	11:30	11:30
12:00	12:00	12:00	12:00
12:30	12:30	12:30	12:30
1:00	1:00	1:00	1:00
1:30	1:30	1:30	1:30
2:00	2:00	2:00	2:00
2:30	2:30	2:30	2:30
3:00	3:00	3:00	3:00
3:30	3:30	3:30	3:30
4:00	4:00	4:00	4:00
4:30	4:30	4:30	4:30
5:00	5:00	5:00	5:00
5:30	5:30	5:30	5:30
6:00	6:00	6:00	6:00
6:30	6:30	6:30	6:30
7:00	7:00	7:00	7:00
7:30	7:30	7:30	7:30
8:00	8:00	8:00	8:00
8:30	8:30	8:30	8:30
9:00	9:00	9:00	9:00
9:30	9:30	9:30	9:30
10:00	10:00	10:00	10:00
10:30	10:30	10:30	10:30
11:00	11:00	11:00	11:00

( )	( )	( )	( )

WEEKLY REFLECTION

• •

1) What was my greatest accomplishment this week?

2) Who or what am I grateful for?

3) What activity from this last week took away from my focus and time?

4) What is one thing I can do to be better prepared for this week?

5) What am I looking forward to during the upcoming week?

BRAINSTORM

FINANCIAL CHECKBOX

Questions	Yes	No
Did I remain on budget this week?		
Did I buy what I needed over what I wanted?		
If you got paid this week, did you place 10% of it in your savings?		
Have I taken a percentage (1%-10%) to donate?		
Did I use my credit card wisely this week?		

How can I manage my money more wisely this week?

MONTHLY REFLECTION

· ·

Write 5 things you accomplished this month:

1.

2.

3.

4.

5.

QUESTIONS

1) What did I learn about myself this month?

2) What tasks are left over from this month that are lingering and need to get done?

3. Did I take care of myself?

4) What could I have done differently this past month?

5) What areas can I (still) improve on?

6) What experiences can I treasure?

7) What challenged me and how did I overcome the challenge?

8) What specific habits and/or rituals could I develop this month to support my vision?

MONTH OF:	SUNDAY	MONDAY	TUESDAY
This Month's Goal			
Important Events or Reminders to Transfer to My Phone			
1.			
2.			
3.			
4.			
5.			
6.			
7.			
8.			
9.			
10.			

PROJECT NAME	CLASS & INSTRUCTOR	IMPORTANT DATES	DEADLINES
1.			
2.			
3.			
4.			

WEDNESDAY	THURSDAY	FRIDAY	SATURDAY

BRAINSTORM

Week of:	Sunday		Monday		Tuesday	
This Week's Goal	S		S		S	
	A		A		A	
	V		V		V	
	E		E		E	
	R		R		R	
	S		S		S	
Intention for the Day	◆		◆		◆	
Grateful for …	◆		◆		◆	

Don't wait. The time will never be just right.

—NAPOLEON HILL

	Sunday	Monday	Tuesday
	5:00	5:00	5:00
	5:30	5:30	5:30
	6:00	6:00	6:00
	6:30	6:30	6:30
	7:00	7:00	7:00
	7:30	7:30	7:30
	8:00	8:00	8:00
	8:30	8:30	8:30
	9:00	9:00	9:00
	9:30	9:30	9:30
	10:00	10:00	10:00
	10:30	10:30	10:30
	11:00	11:00	11:00
	11:30	11:30	11:30
	12:00	12:00	12:00
	12:30	12:30	12:30
	1:00	1:00	1:00
	1:30	1:30	1:30
	2:00	2:00	2:00
	2:30	2:30	2:30
	3:00	3:00	3:00
	3:30	3:30	3:30
	4:00	4:00	4:00
	4:30	4:30	4:30
	5:00	5:00	5:00
	5:30	5:30	5:30
	6:00	6:00	6:00
	6:30	6:30	6:30
	7:00	7:00	7:00
	7:30	7:30	7:30
	8:00	8:00	8:00
	8:30	8:30	8:30
	9:00	9:00	9:00
	9:30	9:30	9:30
	10:00	10:00	10:00
	10:30	10:30	10:30
	11:00	11:00	11:00

TO-DO LIST

Highest Priority

Definite Priority

Lowest Priority

Habit to Work on This Week

Ready for tomorrow?	( )	( )	( )
ALARM			
CLOTHES/BACKPACK			
GLASS OF WATER			
SAVERS PREP			
BEDTIME AFFIRMATIONS			

Wednesday	Thursday	Friday	Saturday
S	S	S	S
A	A	A	A
V	V	V	V
E	E	E	E
R	R	R	R
S	S	S	S
◆	◆	◆	◆
◆	◆	◆	◆

Wednesday		Thursday		Friday		Saturday	
5:00		5:00		5:00		5:00	
5:30		5:30		5:30		5:30	
6:00		6:00		6:00		6:00	
6:30		6:30		6:30		6:30	
7:00		7:00		7:00		7:00	
7:30		7:30		7:30		7:30	
8:00		8:00		8:00		8:00	
8:30		8:30		8:30		8:30	
9:00		9:00		9:00		9:00	
9:30		9:30		9:30		9:30	
10:00		10:00		10:00		10:00	
10:30		10:30		10:30		10:30	
11:00		11:00		11:00		11:00	
11:30		11:30		11:30		11:30	
12:00		12:00		12:00		12:00	
12:30		12:30		12:30		12:30	
1:00		1:00		1:00		1:00	
1:30		1:30		1:30		1:30	
2:00		2:00		2:00		2:00	
2:30		2:30		2:30		2:30	
3:00		3:00		3:00		3:00	
3:30		3:30		3:30		3:30	
4:00		4:00		4:00		4:00	
4:30		4:30		4:30		4:30	
5:00		5:00		5:00		5:00	
5:30		5:30		5:30		5:30	
6:00		6:00		6:00		6:00	
6:30		6:30		6:30		6:30	
7:00		7:00		7:00		7:00	
7:30		7:30		7:30		7:30	
8:00		8:00		8:00		8:00	
8:30		8:30		8:30		8:30	
9:00		9:00		9:00		9:00	
9:30		9:30		9:30		9:30	
10:00		10:00		10:00		10:00	
10:30		10:30		10:30		10:30	
11:00		11:00		11:00		11:00	
	( )		( )		( )		( )

WEEKLY REFLECTION

....

1) What was my greatest accomplishment this week?

2) Who or what am I grateful for?

3) What activity from this last week took away from my focus and time?

4) What is one thing I can do to be better prepared for this week?

5) What am I looking forward to during the upcoming week?

BRAINSTORM

FINANCIAL CHECKBOX

Questions	Yes	No
Did I remain on budget this week?		
Did I buy what I needed over what I wanted?		
If you got paid this week, did you place 10% of it in your savings?		
Have I taken a percentage (1%-10%) to donate?		
Did I use my credit card wisely this week?		

How can I manage my money more wisely this week?

Week of:	Sunday		Monday		Tuesday	
This Week's Goal	S		S		S	
	A		A		A	
	V		V		V	
	E		E		E	
	R		R		R	
	S		S		S	
Intention for the Day	◆		◆		◆	
Grateful for ...	◆		◆		◆	

Everything you've ever wanted is on the other side of fear.

–GEORGE ADDAIR

TO-DO LIST		Sunday		Monday		Tuesday
Highest Priority	5:00		5:00		5:00	
	5:30		5:30		5:30	
	6:00		6:00		6:00	
	6:30		6:30		6:30	
	7:00		7:00		7:00	
	7:30		7:30		7:30	
	8:00		8:00		8:00	
	8:30		8:30		8:30	
	9:00		9:00		9:00	
	9:30		9:30		9:30	
	10:00		10:00		10:00	
	10:30		10:30		10:30	
	11:00		11:00		11:00	
	11:30		11:30		11:30	
	12:00		12:00		12:00	
	12:30		12:30		12:30	
	1:00		1:00		1:00	
Definite Priority	1:30		1:30		1:30	
	2:00		2:00		2:00	
	2:30		2:30		2:30	
	3:00		3:00		3:00	
	3:30		3:30		3:30	
	4:00		4:00		4:00	
Lowest Priority	4:30		4:30		4:30	
	5:00		5:00		5:00	
	5:30		5:30		5:30	
	6:00		6:00		6:00	
	6:30		6:30		6:30	
	7:00		7:00		7:00	
	7:30		7:30		7:30	
Habit to Work on This Week	8:00		8:00		8:00	
	8:30		8:30		8:30	
	9:00		9:00		9:00	
	9:30		9:30		9:30	
	10:00		10:00		10:00	
	10:30		10:30		10:30	
	11:00		11:00		11:00	

Ready for tomorrow?	( )	( )	( )
ALARM			
CLOTHES/BACKPACK			
GLASS OF WATER			
SAVERS PREP			
BEDTIME AFFIRMATIONS			

Wednesday	Thursday	Friday	Saturday
S	S	S	S
A	A	A	A
V	V	V	V
E	E	E	E
R	R	R	R
S	S	S	S
◆	◆	◆	◆
◆	◆	◆	◆

Wednesday	Thursday	Friday	Saturday
5:00	5:00	5:00	5:00
5:30	5:30	5:30	5:30
6:00	6:00	6:00	6:00
6:30	6:30	6:30	6:30
7:00	7:00	7:00	7:00
7:30	7:30	7:30	7:30
8:00	8:00	8:00	8:00
8:30	8:30	8:30	8:30
9:00	9:00	9:00	9:00
9:30	9:30	9:30	9:30
10:00	10:00	10:00	10:00
10:30	10:30	10:30	10:30
11:00	11:00	11:00	11:00
11:30	11:30	11:30	11:30
12:00	12:00	12:00	12:00
12:30	12:30	12:30	12:30
1:00	1:00	1:00	1:00
1:30	1:30	1:30	1:30
2:00	2:00	2:00	2:00
2:30	2:30	2:30	2:30
3:00	3:00	3:00	3:00
3:30	3:30	3:30	3:30
4:00	4:00	4:00	4:00
4:30	4:30	4:30	4:30
5:00	5:00	5:00	5:00
5:30	5:30	5:30	5:30
6:00	6:00	6:00	6:00
6:30	6:30	6:30	6:30
7:00	7:00	7:00	7:00
7:30	7:30	7:30	7:30
8:00	8:00	8:00	8:00
8:30	8:30	8:30	8:30
9:00	9:00	9:00	9:00
9:30	9:30	9:30	9:30
10:00	10:00	10:00	10:00
10:30	10:30	10:30	10:30
11:00	11:00	11:00	11:00

( )	( )	( )	( )

WEEKLY REFLECTION

. . . .

1) What was my greatest accomplishment this week?

2) Who or what am I grateful for?

3) What activity from this last week took away from my focus and time?

4) What is one thing I can do to be better prepared for this week?

5) What am I looking forward to during the upcoming week?

BRAINSTORM

FINANCIAL CHECKBOX

Questions	Yes	No
Did I remain on budget this week?		
Did I buy what I needed over what I wanted?		
If you got paid this week, did you place 10% of it in your savings?		
Have I taken a percentage (1%-10%) to donate?		
Did I use my credit card wisely this week?		

How can I manage my money more wisely this week?

Week of:		Sunday		Monday		Tuesday
This Week's Goal		S		S		S
		A		A		A
		V		V		V
		E		E		E
		R		R		R
		S		S		S
Intention for the Day		◆		◆		◆
Grateful for ...		◆		◆		◆

A year from now you may wish you had started today.

—KAREN LAMB

TO-DO LIST		Sunday		Monday		Tuesday
Highest Priority	5:00		5:00		5:00	
	5:30		5:30		5:30	
	6:00		6:00		6:00	
	6:30		6:30		6:30	
	7:00		7:00		7:00	
	7:30		7:30		7:30	
	8:00		8:00		8:00	
	8:30		8:30		8:30	
	9:00		9:00		9:00	
	9:30		9:30		9:30	
	10:00		10:00		10:00	
	10:30		10:30		10:30	
	11:00		11:00		11:00	
	11:30		11:30		11:30	
	12:00		12:00		12:00	
	12:30		12:30		12:30	
	1:00		1:00		1:00	
Definite Priority	1:30		1:30		1:30	
	2:00		2:00		2:00	
	2:30		2:30		2:30	
	3:00		3:00		3:00	
	3:30		3:30		3:30	
	4:00		4:00		4:00	
Lowest Priority	4:30		4:30		4:30	
	5:00		5:00		5:00	
	5:30		5:30		5:30	
	6:00		6:00		6:00	
	6:30		6:30		6:30	
	7:00		7:00		7:00	
	7:30		7:30		7:30	
Habit to Work on This Week	8:00		8:00		8:00	
	8:30		8:30		8:30	
	9:00		9:00		9:00	
	9:30		9:30		9:30	
	10:00		10:00		10:00	
	10:30		10:30		10:30	
	11:00		11:00		11:00	

Ready for tomorrow?	( )	( )	( )
ALARM			
CLOTHES/BACKPACK			
GLASS OF WATER			
SAVERS PREP			
BEDTIME AFFIRMATIONS			

Wednesday		Thursday		Friday		Saturday	
S		S		S		S	
A		A		A		A	
V		V		V		V	
E		E		E		E	
R		R		R		R	
S		S		S		S	
◆		◆		◆		◆	
◆		◆		◆		◆	
5:00		5:00		5:00		5:00	
5:30		5:30		5:30		5:30	
6:00		6:00		6:00		6:00	
6:30		6:30		6:30		6:30	
7:00		7:00		7:00		7:00	
7:30		7:30		7:30		7:30	
8:00		8:00		8:00		8:00	
8:30		8:30		8:30		8:30	
9:00		9:00		9:00		9:00	
9:30		9:30		9:30		9:30	
10:00		10:00		10:00		10:00	
10:30		10:30		10:30		10:30	
11:00		11:00		11:00		11:00	
11:30		11:30		11:30		11:30	
12:00		12:00		12:00		12:00	
12:30		12:30		12:30		12:30	
1:00		1:00		1:00		1:00	
1:30		1:30		1:30		1:30	
2:00		2:00		2:00		2:00	
2:30		2:30		2:30		2:30	
3:00		3:00		3:00		3:00	
3:30		3:30		3:30		3:30	
4:00		4:00		4:00		4:00	
4:30		4:30		4:30		4:30	
5:00		5:00		5:00		5:00	
5:30		5:30		5:30		5:30	
6:00		6:00		6:00		6:00	
6:30		6:30		6:30		6:30	
7:00		7:00		7:00		7:00	
7:30		7:30		7:30		7:30	
8:00		8:00		8:00		8:00	
8:30		8:30		8:30		8:30	
9:00		9:00		9:00		9:00	
9:30		9:30		9:30		9:30	
10:00		10:00		10:00		10:00	
10:30		10:30		10:30		10:30	
11:00		11:00		11:00		11:00	
	( )		( )		( )		( )

WEEKLY REFLECTION

• •

1) What was my greatest accomplishment this week?

2) Who or what am I grateful for?

3) What activity from this last week took away from my focus and time?

4) What is one thing I can do to be better prepared for this week?

5) What am I looking forward to during the upcoming week?

BRAINSTORM

FINANCIAL CHECKBOX

Questions	Yes	No
Did I remain on budget this week?		
Did I buy what I needed over what I wanted?		
If you got paid this week, did you place 10% of it in your savings?		
Have I taken a percentage (1%-10%) to donate?		
Did I use my credit card wisely this week?		

How can I manage my money more wisely this week?

Week of:	Sunday	Monday	Tuesday
This Week's Goal	S	S	S
	A	A	A
	V	V	V
	E	E	E
	R	R	R
	S	S	S
Intention for the Day	◆	◆	◆
Grateful for ...	◆	◆	◆

	Sunday	Monday	Tuesday
	5:00	5:00	5:00
	5:30	5:30	5:30
It is never too late to be what you might have been.	6:00	6:00	6:00
	6:30	6:30	6:30
—GEORGE ELIOT	7:00	7:00	7:00
	7:30	7:30	7:30
	8:00	8:00	8:00
	8:30	8:30	8:30
	9:00	9:00	9:00
	9:30	9:30	9:30
TO-DO LIST	10:00	10:00	10:00
Highest Priority	10:30	10:30	10:30
	11:00	11:00	11:00
	11:30	11:30	11:30
	12:00	12:00	12:00
	12:30	12:30	12:30
	1:00	1:00	1:00
Definite Priority	1:30	1:30	1:30
	2:00	2:00	2:00
	2:30	2:30	2:30
	3:00	3:00	3:00
	3:30	3:30	3:30
	4:00	4:00	4:00
Lowest Priority	4:30	4:30	4:30
	5:00	5:00	5:00
	5:30	5:30	5:30
	6:00	6:00	6:00
	6:30	6:30	6:30
	7:00	7:00	7:00
	7:30	7:30	7:30
Habit to Work on This Week	8:00	8:00	8:00
	8:30	8:30	8:30
	9:00	9:00	9:00
	9:30	9:30	9:30
	10:00	10:00	10:00
	10:30	10:30	10:30
	11:00	11:00	11:00

Ready for tomorrow?	( )	( )	( )
ALARM			
CLOTHES/BACKPACK			
GLASS OF WATER			
SAVERS PREP			
BEDTIME AFFIRMATIONS			

Wednesday		Thursday		Friday		Saturday	
S		S		S		S	
A		A		A		A	
V		V		V		V	
E		E		E		E	
R		R		R		R	
S		S		S		S	
◆		◆		◆		◆	
◆		◆		◆		◆	
5:00		5:00		5:00		5:00	
5:30		5:30		5:30		5:30	
6:00		6:00		6:00		6:00	
6:30		6:30		6:30		6:30	
7:00		7:00		7:00		7:00	
7:30		7:30		7:30		7:30	
8:00		8:00		8:00		8:00	
8:30		8:30		8:30		8:30	
9:00		9:00		9:00		9:00	
9:30		9:30		9:30		9:30	
10:00		10:00		10:00		10:00	
10:30		10:30		10:30		10:30	
11:00		11:00		11:00		11:00	
11:30		11:30		11:30		11:30	
12:00		12:00		12:00		12:00	
12:30		12:30		12:30		12:30	
1:00		1:00		1:00		1:00	
1:30		1:30		1:30		1:30	
2:00		2:00		2:00		2:00	
2:30		2:30		2:30		2:30	
3:00		3:00		3:00		3:00	
3:30		3:30		3:30		3:30	
4:00		4:00		4:00		4:00	
4:30		4:30		4:30		4:30	
5:00		5:00		5:00		5:00	
5:30		5:30		5:30		5:30	
6:00		6:00		6:00		6:00	
6:30		6:30		6:30		6:30	
7:00		7:00		7:00		7:00	
7:30		7:30		7:30		7:30	
8:00		8:00		8:00		8:00	
8:30		8:30		8:30		8:30	
9:00		9:00		9:00		9:00	
9:30		9:30		9:30		9:30	
10:00		10:00		10:00		10:00	
10:30		10:30		10:30		10:30	
11:00		11:00		11:00		11:00	
	( )		( )		( )		( )

WEEKLY REFLECTION

· ·

1) What was my greatest accomplishment this week?

2) Who or what am I grateful for?

3) What activity from this last week took away from my focus and time?

4) What is one thing I can do to be better prepared for this week?

5) What am I looking forward to during the upcoming week?

BRAINSTORM

FINANCIAL CHECKBOX

Questions	Yes	No
Did I remain on budget this week?		
Did I buy what I needed over what I wanted?		
If you got paid this week, did you place 10% of it in your savings?		
Have I taken a percentage (1%-10%) to donate?		
Did I use my credit card wisely this week?		

How can I manage my money more wisely this week?

Week of:	Sunday	Monday	Tuesday
This Week's Goal	S	S	S
	A	A	A
	V	V	V
	E	E	E
	R	R	R
	S	S	S
Intention for the Day	◆	◆	◆
Grateful for ...	◆	◆	◆

What we fear doing most is usually what we most need to do.

—TIM FERRISS

TO-DO LIST			
Highest Priority			
Definite Priority			
Lowest Priority			
Habit to Work on This Week			

Time	Sunday	Monday	Tuesday
5:00		5:00	5:00
5:30		5:30	5:30
6:00		6:00	6:00
6:30		6:30	6:30
7:00		7:00	7:00
7:30		7:30	7:30
8:00		8:00	8:00
8:30		8:30	8:30
9:00		9:00	9:00
9:30		9:30	9:30
10:00		10:00	10:00
10:30		10:30	10:30
11:00		11:00	11:00
11:30		11:30	11:30
12:00		12:00	12:00
12:30		12:30	12:30
1:00		1:00	1:00
1:30		1:30	1:30
2:00		2:00	2:00
2:30		2:30	2:30
3:00		3:00	3:00
3:30		3:30	3:30
4:00		4:00	4:00
4:30		4:30	4:30
5:00		5:00	5:00
5:30		5:30	5:30
6:00		6:00	6:00
6:30		6:30	6:30
7:00		7:00	7:00
7:30		7:30	7:30
8:00		8:00	8:00
8:30		8:30	8:30
9:00		9:00	9:00
9:30		9:30	9:30
10:00		10:00	10:00
10:30		10:30	10:30
11:00		11:00	11:00

Ready for tomorrow?	( )	( )	( )
ALARM			
CLOTHES/BACKPACK			
GLASS OF WATER			
SAVERS PREP			
BEDTIME AFFIRMATIONS			

Wednesday		Thursday		Friday		Saturday	
S		S		S		S	
A		A		A		A	
V		V		V		V	
E		E		E		E	
R		R		R		R	
S		S		S		S	
◆		◆		◆		◆	
◆		◆		◆		◆	
5:00		5:00		5:00		5:00	
5:30		5:30		5:30		5:30	
6:00		6:00		6:00		6:00	
6:30		6:30		6:30		6:30	
7:00		7:00		7:00		7:00	
7:30		7:30		7:30		7:30	
8:00		8:00		8:00		8:00	
8:30		8:30		8:30		8:30	
9:00		9:00		9:00		9:00	
9:30		9:30		9:30		9:30	
10:00		10:00		10:00		10:00	
10:30		10:30		10:30		10:30	
11:00		11:00		11:00		11:00	
11:30		11:30		11:30		11:30	
12:00		12:00		12:00		12:00	
12:30		12:30		12:30		12:30	
1:00		1:00		1:00		1:00	
1:30		1:30		1:30		1:30	
2:00		2:00		2:00		2:00	
2:30		2:30		2:30		2:30	
3:00		3:00		3:00		3:00	
3:30		3:30		3:30		3:30	
4:00		4:00		4:00		4:00	
4:30		4:30		4:30		4:30	
5:00		5:00		5:00		5:00	
5:30		5:30		5:30		5:30	
6:00		6:00		6:00		6:00	
6:30		6:30		6:30		6:30	
7:00		7:00		7:00		7:00	
7:30		7:30		7:30		7:30	
8:00		8:00		8:00		8:00	
8:30		8:30		8:30		8:30	
9:00		9:00		9:00		9:00	
9:30		9:30		9:30		9:30	
10:00		10:00		10:00		10:00	
10:30		10:30		10:30		10:30	
11:00		11:00		11:00		11:00	
( )		( )		( )		( )	

WEEKLY REFLECTION

• •

1) What was my greatest accomplishment this week?

2) Who or what am I grateful for?

3) What activity from this last week took away from my focus and time?

4) What is one thing I can do to be better prepared for this week?

5) What am I looking forward to during the upcoming week?

BRAINSTORM

FINANCIAL CHECKBOX

Questions	Yes	No
Did I remain on budget this week?		
Did I buy what I needed over what I wanted?		
If you got paid this week, did you place 10% of it in your savings?		
Have I taken a percentage (1%-10%) to donate?		
Did I use my credit card wisely this week?		
How can I manage my money more wisely this week?		

MONTHLY REFLECTION

· ·

Write 5 things you accomplished this month:

1.

2.

3.

4.

5.

QUESTIONS

1) What did I learn about myself this month?

2) What tasks are left over from this month that are lingering and need to get done?

3. Did I take care of myself?

4) What could I have done differently this past month?

5) What areas can I (still) improve on?

6) What experiences can I treasure?

7) What challenged me and how did I overcome the challenge?

8) What specific habits and/or rituals could I develop this month to support my vision?

MONTH OF:	SUNDAY	MONDAY	TUESDAY
This Month's Goal			
Important Events or Reminders to Transfer to My Phone			
1.			
2.			
3.			
4.			
5.			
6.			
7.			
8.			
9.			
10.			

PROJECT NAME	CLASS & INSTRUCTOR	IMPORTANT DATES	DEADLINES
1.			
2.			
3.			
4.			

WEDNESDAY	THURSDAY	FRIDAY	SATURDAY

BRAINSTORM

Week of:		Sunday		Monday		Tuesday	
This Week's Goal		S		S		S	
		A		A		A	
		V		V		V	
		E		E		E	
		R		R		R	
		S		S		S	
Intention for the Day		◆		◆		◆	
Grateful for ...		◆		◆		◆	

> *The more I want to get something done, the less I call it work.*
>
> **—RICHARD BACH**

TO-DO LIST
Highest Priority
Definite Priority
Lowest Priority
Habit to Work on This Week

Time	Sunday	Monday	Tuesday
5:00			
5:30			
6:00			
6:30			
7:00			
7:30			
8:00			
8:30			
9:00			
9:30			
10:00			
10:30			
11:00			
11:30			
12:00			
12:30			
1:00			
1:30			
2:00			
2:30			
3:00			
3:30			
4:00			
4:30			
5:00			
5:30			
6:00			
6:30			
7:00			
7:30			
8:00			
8:30			
9:00			
9:30			
10:00			
10:30			
11:00			

Ready for tomorrow?	( )	( )	( )
ALARM			
CLOTHES/BACKPACK			
GLASS OF WATER			
SAVERS PREP			
BEDTIME AFFIRMATIONS			

Wednesday		Thursday		Friday		Saturday	
S		S		S		S	
A		A		A		A	
V		V		V		V	
E		E		E		E	
R		R		R		R	
S		S		S		S	
◆		◆		◆		◆	
◆		◆		◆		◆	
5:00		5:00		5:00		5:00	
5:30		5:30		5:30		5:30	
6:00		6:00		6:00		6:00	
6:30		6:30		6:30		6:30	
7:00		7:00		7:00		7:00	
7:30		7:30		7:30		7:30	
8:00		8:00		8:00		8:00	
8:30		8:30		8:30		8:30	
9:00		9:00		9:00		9:00	
9:30		9:30		9:30		9:30	
10:00		10:00		10:00		10:00	
10:30		10:30		10:30		10:30	
11:00		11:00		11:00		11:00	
11:30		11:30		11:30		11:30	
12:00		12:00		12:00		12:00	
12:30		12:30		12:30		12:30	
1:00		1:00		1:00		1:00	
1:30		1:30		1:30		1:30	
2:00		2:00		2:00		2:00	
2:30		2:30		2:30		2:30	
3:00		3:00		3:00		3:00	
3:30		3:30		3:30		3:30	
4:00		4:00		4:00		4:00	
4:30		4:30		4:30		4:30	
5:00		5:00		5:00		5:00	
5:30		5:30		5:30		5:30	
6:00		6:00		6:00		6:00	
6:30		6:30		6:30		6:30	
7:00		7:00		7:00		7:00	
7:30		7:30		7:30		7:30	
8:00		8:00		8:00		8:00	
8:30		8:30		8:30		8:30	
9:00		9:00		9:00		9:00	
9:30		9:30		9:30		9:30	
10:00		10:00		10:00		10:00	
10:30		10:30		10:30		10:30	
11:00		11:00		11:00		11:00	
	( )		( )		( )		( )

WEEKLY REFLECTION

. . . .

1) What was my greatest accomplishment this week?

2) Who or what am I grateful for?

3) What activity from this last week took away from my focus and time?

4) What is one thing I can do to be better prepared for this week?

5) What am I looking forward to during the upcoming week?

BRAINSTORM

FINANCIAL CHECKBOX

Questions	Yes	No
Did I remain on budget this week?		
Did I buy what I needed over what I wanted?		
If you got paid this week, did you place 10% of it in your savings?		
Have I taken a percentage (1%-10%) to donate?		
Did I use my credit card wisely this week?		

How can I manage my money more wisely this week?

Week of:	Sunday		Monday		Tuesday	
This Week's Goal	S		S		S	
	A		A		A	
	V		V		V	
	E		E		E	
	R		R		R	
	S		S		S	
Intention for the Day	◆		◆		◆	
Grateful for ...	◆		◆		◆	

The best way to predict your future is to create it.

–ABRAHAM LINCOLN

TO-DO LIST	Sunday	Monday	Tuesday
Highest Priority	5:00	5:00	5:00
	5:30	5:30	5:30
	6:00	6:00	6:00
	6:30	6:30	6:30
	7:00	7:00	7:00
	7:30	7:30	7:30
	8:00	8:00	8:00
	8:30	8:30	8:30
	9:00	9:00	9:00
	9:30	9:30	9:30
	10:00	10:00	10:00
	10:30	10:30	10:30
	11:00	11:00	11:00
	11:30	11:30	11:30
	12:00	12:00	12:00
	12:30	12:30	12:30
	1:00	1:00	1:00
Definite Priority	1:30	1:30	1:30
	2:00	2:00	2:00
	2:30	2:30	2:30
	3:00	3:00	3:00
	3:30	3:30	3:30
	4:00	4:00	4:00
Lowest Priority	4:30	4:30	4:30
	5:00	5:00	5:00
	5:30	5:30	5:30
	6:00	6:00	6:00
	6:30	6:30	6:30
	7:00	7:00	7:00
	7:30	7:30	7:30
Habit to Work on This Week	8:00	8:00	8:00
	8:30	8:30	8:30
	9:00	9:00	9:00
	9:30	9:30	9:30
	10:00	10:00	10:00
	10:30	10:30	10:30
	11:00	11:00	11:00

Ready for tomorrow?	( )	( )	( )
ALARM			
CLOTHES/BACKPACK			
GLASS OF WATER			
SAVERS PREP			
BEDTIME AFFIRMATIONS			

Wednesday		Thursday		Friday		Saturday	
S		S		S		S	
A		A		A		A	
V		V		V		V	
E		E		E		E	
R		R		R		R	
S		S		S		S	
◆		◆		◆		◆	
◆		◆		◆		◆	
5:00		5:00		5:00		5:00	
5:30		5:30		5:30		5:30	
6:00		6:00		6:00		6:00	
6:30		6:30		6:30		6:30	
7:00		7:00		7:00		7:00	
7:30		7:30		7:30		7:30	
8:00		8:00		8:00		8:00	
8:30		8:30		8:30		8:30	
9:00		9:00		9:00		9:00	
9:30		9:30		9:30		9:30	
10:00		10:00		10:00		10:00	
10:30		10:30		10:30		10:30	
11:00		11:00		11:00		11:00	
11:30		11:30		11:30		11:30	
12:00		12:00		12:00		12:00	
12:30		12:30		12:30		12:30	
1:00		1:00		1:00		1:00	
1:30		1:30		1:30		1:30	
2:00		2:00		2:00		2:00	
2:30		2:30		2:30		2:30	
3:00		3:00		3:00		3:00	
3:30		3:30		3:30		3:30	
4:00		4:00		4:00		4:00	
4:30		4:30		4:30		4:30	
5:00		5:00		5:00		5:00	
5:30		5:30		5:30		5:30	
6:00		6:00		6:00		6:00	
6:30		6:30		6:30		6:30	
7:00		7:00		7:00		7:00	
7:30		7:30		7:30		7:30	
8:00		8:00		8:00		8:00	
8:30		8:30		8:30		8:30	
9:00		9:00		9:00		9:00	
9:30		9:30		9:30		9:30	
10:00		10:00		10:00		10:00	
10:30		10:30		10:30		10:30	
11:00		11:00		11:00		11:00	
	( )		( )		( )		( )

WEEKLY REFLECTION

....

1) What was my greatest accomplishment this week?

2) Who or what am I grateful for?

3) What activity from this last week took away from my focus and time?

4) What is one thing I can do to be better prepared for this week?

5) What am I looking forward to during the upcoming week?

BRAINSTORM

FINANCIAL CHECKBOX

Questions	Yes	No
Did I remain on budget this week?		
Did I buy what I needed over what I wanted?		
If you got paid this week, did you place 10% of it in your savings?		
Have I taken a percentage (1%-10%) to donate?		
Did I use my credit card wisely this week?		

How can I manage my money more wisely this week?

Week of:	Sunday	Monday	Tuesday	
This Week's Goal	S	S	S	
	A	A	A	
	V	V	V	
	E	E	E	
	R	R	R	
	S	S	S	
Intention for the Day	◆	◆	◆	
Grateful for ...	◆	◆	◆	

		Sunday		Monday		Tuesday
	5:00		5:00		5:00	
	5:30		5:30		5:30	
The dreamers are	6:00		6:00		6:00	
the saviors of	6:30		6:30		6:30	
the world.	7:00		7:00		7:00	
	7:30		7:30		7:30	
—JAMES ALLEN	8:00		8:00		8:00	
	8:30		8:30		8:30	
	9:00		9:00		9:00	
	9:30		9:30		9:30	
TO-DO LIST	10:00		10:00		10:00	
Highest Priority	10:30		10:30		10:30	
	11:00		11:00		11:00	
	11:30		11:30		11:30	
	12:00		12:00		12:00	
	12:30		12:30		12:30	
	1:00		1:00		1:00	
Definite Priority	1:30		1:30		1:30	
	2:00		2:00		2:00	
	2:30		2:30		2:30	
	3:00		3:00		3:00	
	3:30		3:30		3:30	
	4:00		4:00		4:00	
Lowest Priority	4:30		4:30		4:30	
	5:00		5:00		5:00	
	5:30		5:30		5:30	
	6:00		6:00		6:00	
	6:30		6:30		6:30	
	7:00		7:00		7:00	
	7:30		7:30		7:30	
Habit to Work on This Week	8:00		8:00		8:00	
	8:30		8:30		8:30	
	9:00		9:00		9:00	
	9:30		9:30		9:30	
	10:00		10:00		10:00	
	10:30		10:30		10:30	
	11:00		11:00		11:00	

Ready for tomorrow?	( )	( )	( )
ALARM			
CLOTHES/BACKPACK			
GLASS OF WATER			
SAVERS PREP			
BEDTIME AFFIRMATIONS			

Wednesday	Thursday	Friday	Saturday
S	S	S	S
A	A	A	A
V	V	V	V
E	E	E	E
R	R	R	R
S	S	S	S

◆	◆	◆	◆
◆	◆	◆	◆

Wednesday	Thursday	Friday	Saturday
5:00	5:00	5:00	5:00
5:30	5:30	5:30	5:30
6:00	6:00	6:00	6:00
6:30	6:30	6:30	6:30
7:00	7:00	7:00	7:00
7:30	7:30	7:30	7:30
8:00	8:00	8:00	8:00
8:30	8:30	8:30	8:30
9:00	9:00	9:00	9:00
9:30	9:30	9:30	9:30
10:00	10:00	10:00	10:00
10:30	10:30	10:30	10:30
11:00	11:00	11:00	11:00
11:30	11:30	11:30	11:30
12:00	12:00	12:00	12:00
12:30	12:30	12:30	12:30
1:00	1:00	1:00	1:00
1:30	1:30	1:30	1:30
2:00	2:00	2:00	2:00
2:30	2:30	2:30	2:30
3:00	3:00	3:00	3:00
3:30	3:30	3:30	3:30
4:00	4:00	4:00	4:00
4:30	4:30	4:30	4:30
5:00	5:00	5:00	5:00
5:30	5:30	5:30	5:30
6:00	6:00	6:00	6:00
6:30	6:30	6:30	6:30
7:00	7:00	7:00	7:00
7:30	7:30	7:30	7:30
8:00	8:00	8:00	8:00
8:30	8:30	8:30	8:30
9:00	9:00	9:00	9:00
9:30	9:30	9:30	9:30
10:00	10:00	10:00	10:00
10:30	10:30	10:30	10:30
11:00	11:00	11:00	11:00

( )	( )	( )	( )

WEEKLY REFLECTION

• •

1) What was my greatest accomplishment this week?

2) Who or what am I grateful for?

3) What activity from this last week took away from my focus and time?

4) What is one thing I can do to be better prepared for this week?

5) What am I looking forward to during the upcoming week?

BRAINSTORM

FINANCIAL CHECKBOX

Questions	Yes	No
Did I remain on budget this week?		
Did I buy what I needed over what I wanted?		
If you got paid this week, did you place 10% of it in your savings?		
Have I taken a percentage (1%-10%) to donate?		
Did I use my credit card wisely this week?		

How can I manage my money more wisely this week?

Week of:	Sunday		Monday		Tuesday	
This Week's Goal	S		S		S	
	A		A		A	
	V		V		V	
	E		E		E	
	R		R		R	
	S		S		S	
Intention for the Day	◆		◆		◆	
Grateful for ...	◆		◆		◆	

There are no short cuts to any place worth going.

—BEVERLY SILLS

	Sunday	Monday	Tuesday
	5:00	5:00	5:00
	5:30	5:30	5:30
	6:00	6:00	6:00
	6:30	6:30	6:30
	7:00	7:00	7:00
	7:30	7:30	7:30
	8:00	8:00	8:00
	8:30	8:30	8:30
	9:00	9:00	9:00
	9:30	9:30	9:30
	10:00	10:00	10:00
	10:30	10:30	10:30
	11:00	11:00	11:00
	11:30	11:30	11:30
	12:00	12:00	12:00
	12:30	12:30	12:30
	1:00	1:00	1:00
	1:30	1:30	1:30
	2:00	2:00	2:00
	2:30	2:30	2:30
	3:00	3:00	3:00
	3:30	3:30	3:30
	4:00	4:00	4:00
	4:30	4:30	4:30
	5:00	5:00	5:00
	5:30	5:30	5:30
	6:00	6:00	6:00
	6:30	6:30	6:30
	7:00	7:00	7:00
	7:30	7:30	7:30
	8:00	8:00	8:00
	8:30	8:30	8:30
	9:00	9:00	9:00
	9:30	9:30	9:30
	10:00	10:00	10:00
	10:30	10:30	10:30
	11:00	11:00	11:00

TO-DO LIST

Highest Priority

Definite Priority

Lowest Priority

Habit to Work on This Week

Ready for tomorrow?	( )	( )	( )
ALARM			
CLOTHES/BACKPACK			
GLASS OF WATER			
SAVERS PREP			
BEDTIME AFFIRMATIONS			

Wednesday		Thursday		Friday		Saturday	
S		S		S		S	
A		A		A		A	
V		V		V		V	
E		E		E		E	
R		R		R		R	
S		S		S		S	
◆		◆		◆		◆	
◆		◆		◆		◆	
5:00		5:00		5:00		5:00	
5:30		5:30		5:30		5:30	
6:00		6:00		6:00		6:00	
6:30		6:30		6:30		6:30	
7:00		7:00		7:00		7:00	
7:30		7:30		7:30		7:30	
8:00		8:00		8:00		8:00	
8:30		8:30		8:30		8:30	
9:00		9:00		9:00		9:00	
9:30		9:30		9:30		9:30	
10:00		10:00		10:00		10:00	
10:30		10:30		10:30		10:30	
11:00		11:00		11:00		11:00	
11:30		11:30		11:30		11:30	
12:00		12:00		12:00		12:00	
12:30		12:30		12:30		12:30	
1:00		1:00		1:00		1:00	
1:30		1:30		1:30		1:30	
2:00		2:00		2:00		2:00	
2:30		2:30		2:30		2:30	
3:00		3:00		3:00		3:00	
3:30		3:30		3:30		3:30	
4:00		4:00		4:00		4:00	
4:30		4:30		4:30		4:30	
5:00		5:00		5:00		5:00	
5:30		5:30		5:30		5:30	
6:00		6:00		6:00		6:00	
6:30		6:30		6:30		6:30	
7:00		7:00		7:00		7:00	
7:30		7:30		7:30		7:30	
8:00		8:00		8:00		8:00	
8:30		8:30		8:30		8:30	
9:00		9:00		9:00		9:00	
9:30		9:30		9:30		9:30	
10:00		10:00		10:00		10:00	
10:30		10:30		10:30		10:30	
11:00		11:00		11:00			
( )		( )		( )		( )	

WEEKLY REFLECTION

••

1) What was my greatest accomplishment this week?

2) Who or what am I grateful for?

3) What activity from this last week took away from my focus and time?

4) What is one thing I can do to be better prepared for this week?

5) What am I looking forward to during the upcoming week?

BRAINSTORM

FINANCIAL CHECKBOX

Questions	Yes	No
Did I remain on budget this week?		
Did I buy what I needed over what I wanted?		
If you got paid this week, did you place 10% of it in your savings?		
Have I taken a percentage (1%-10%) to donate?		
Did I use my credit card wisely this week?		

How can I manage my money more wisely this week?

Week of:	Sunday	Monday	Tuesday
This Week's Goal	S	S	S
	A	A	A
	V	V	V
	E	E	E
	R	R	R
	S	S	S
Intention for the Day	◆	◆	◆
Grateful for ...	◆	◆	◆

	Sunday	Monday	Tuesday
	5:00	5:00	5:00
Very often a change of self is needed more than a change of scene.	5:30	5:30	5:30
	6:00	6:00	6:00
	6:30	6:30	6:30
	7:00	7:00	7:00
	7:30	7:30	7:30
—ARTHUR CHRISTOPHER BENSON	8:00	8:00	8:00
	8:30	8:30	8:30
	9:00	9:00	9:00
	9:30	9:30	9:30
TO-DO LIST	10:00	10:00	10:00
Highest Priority	10:30	10:30	10:30
	11:00	11:00	11:00
	11:30	11:30	11:30
	12:00	12:00	12:00
	12:30	12:30	12:30
	1:00	1:00	1:00
Definite Priority	1:30	1:30	1:30
	2:00	2:00	2:00
	2:30	2:30	2:30
	3:00	3:00	3:00
	3:30	3:30	3:30
	4:00	4:00	4:00
Lowest Priority	4:30	4:30	4:30
	5:00	5:00	5:00
	5:30	5:30	5:30
	6:00	6:00	6:00
	6:30	6:30	6:30
	7:00	7:00	7:00
	7:30	7:30	7:30
Habit to Work on This Week	8:00	8:00	8:00
	8:30	8:30	8:30
	9:00	9:00	9:00
	9:30	9:30	9:30
	10:00	10:00	10:00
	10:30	10:30	10:30
	11:00	11:00	11:00

Ready for tomorrow?	( )	( )	( )
ALARM			
CLOTHES/BACKPACK			
GLASS OF WATER			
SAVERS PREP			
BEDTIME AFFIRMATIONS			

Wednesday	Thursday	Friday	Saturday
S	S	S	S
A	A	A	A
V	V	V	V
E	E	E	E
R	R	R	R
S	S	S	S

◆	◆	◆	◆
◆	◆	◆	◆

Wednesday	Thursday	Friday	Saturday
5:00	5:00	5:00	5:00
5:30	5:30	5:30	5:30
6:00	6:00	6:00	6:00
6:30	6:30	6:30	6:30
7:00	7:00	7:00	7:00
7:30	7:30	7:30	7:30
8:00	8:00	8:00	8:00
8:30	8:30	8:30	8:30
9:00	9:00	9:00	9:00
9:30	9:30	9:30	9:30
10:00	10:00	10:00	10:00
10:30	10:30	10:30	10:30
11:00	11:00	11:00	11:00
11:30	11:30	11:30	11:30
12:00	12:00	12:00	12:00
12:30	12:30	12:30	12:30
1:00	1:00	1:00	1:00
1:30	1:30	1:30	1:30
2:00	2:00	2:00	2:00
2:30	2:30	2:30	2:30
3:00	3:00	3:00	3:00
3:30	3:30	3:30	3:30
4:00	4:00	4:00	4:00
4:30	4:30	4:30	4:30
5:00	5:00	5:00	5:00
5:30	5:30	5:30	5:30
6:00	6:00	6:00	6:00
6:30	6:30	6:30	6:30
7:00	7:00	7:00	7:00
7:30	7:30	7:30	7:30
8:00	8:00	8:00	8:00
8:30	8:30	8:30	8:30
9:00	9:00	9:00	9:00
9:30	9:30	9:30	9:30
10:00	10:00	10:00	10:00
10:30	10:30	10:30	10:30
11:00	11:00	11:00	

( )	( )	( )	( )

WEEKLY REFLECTION

• •

1) What was my greatest accomplishment this week?

2) Who or what am I grateful for?

3) What activity from this last week took away from my focus and time?

4) What is one thing I can do to be better prepared for this week?

5) What am I looking forward to during the upcoming week?

BRAINSTORM

FINANCIAL CHECKBOX

Questions	Yes	No
Did I remain on budget this week?		
Did I buy what I needed over what I wanted?		
If you got paid this week, did you place 10% of it in your savings?		
Have I taken a percentage (1%-10%) to donate?		
Did I use my credit card wisely this week?		

How can I manage my money more wisely this week?

MONTHLY REFLECTION

....

Write 5 things you accomplished this month:

1.

2.

3.

4.

5.

QUESTIONS

1) What did I learn about myself this month?

2) What tasks are left over from this month that are lingering and need to get done?

3. Did I take care of myself?

4) What could I have done differently this past month?

5) What areas can I (still) improve on?

6) What experiences can I treasure?

7) What challenged me and how did I overcome the challenge?

8) What specific habits and/or rituals could I develop this month to support my vision?

REFERENCES

Sample Affirmations

- I am just as worthy, deserving, and capable of achieving personal and academic success as any other person on earth, and I will prove that today with my actions.

- I am becoming healthier each day because I am committed to making healthy choices for my body and my mind every day.

- Where I *am* is a result of who I *was*, but where I go depends entirely on who I *choose to be* starting today.

- I choose to take 100% responsibility for my own success, because my success depends on my actions and decisions each day.

- I am a hardworking, intelligent student and I committed to excelling in my major and career.

- I am fully committed to dedicating 30–60 minutes to do my Miracle Morning and the Life S.A.V.E.R.S. so that I can continue to become the person I need to be to create everything I want for my life.

- I am fully committed to replace my complaints with words of gratitude, because even in the midst of difficulty, gratitude will bring more appreciation to the present moment than complaining.

- I am grateful for all my wins, and most especially for all my "losses", because each of those experiences hold the knowledge of how I can further improve as a student and as an individual.

- I focus on learning new things and improving my self-awareness daily, and I commit to reading or rereading at least one book to help that effort every month.

- By asking the right questions, I continue to learn more about myself so that I will create a clearer picture of my overall vision.

- I am committed to constant and never-ending improvement in the tasks necessary for the day-to-day functioning of a college student.

Sample Journal Questions

- What is the one thing I want to accomplish today?

- Where can I find more time in my schedule? How might I be able to do that?

- What does a Level 10 post-graduation life look like to me?

- What are my biggest hopes and dreams?

- What is my life's passion?

- What do I love to do?

- What am I best at?

- What problem can I solve?

- How can I add value to the world?

- What dream job do I want to have?

- How might I go about creating a life that I would be happy to call my reality?

- What realization have I had recently?

- How can I be more proactive about my life and my future today?

- What's working that I should *keep doing* (or do more of)?

- What do I need to *start doing* to accelerate results?

- What do I need to *stop doing* immediately that's holding me back from going to the next level?

- What is one habit I can practice to improve health? Productivity? Clarity?

- How will I overcome the obstacles that come my way today?

- What can I feel joy about today?

- What can I feel grateful for this morning?

- How have I improved in these last few weeks?

- Where do I see myself in a year? Two years? Five years?

- What are some changes I'd like to make to my Miracle Morning?

Apps for Meditation

- Headspace

- Calm

- Omvana

- Simply Being

- Insight Timer

BOOKS

On Mindset

- *The Art of Exceptional Living* by Jim Rohn

- *The One Thing: The Surprisingly Simple Truth Behind Extraordinary Results* by Gary Keller and Jay Papasan

- *The 7 Habits of Highly Effective People: Powerful Lessons in Personal Change* by Stephen R. Covey

- *Mastery* by Robert Greene

- *The 4-Hour Workweek: Escape 9–5, Live Anywhere, and Join the New Rich* by Tim Ferriss

- *The Game of Life and How to Play It* by Florence Scovel Shinn

- *The Compound Effect* by Darren Hardy

- *Man's Search for Meaning* by Viktor Frankl

- *Taking Life Head On: How to Love the Life You Have While You Create the Life of Your Dreams* by Hal Elrod

- *Think and Grow Rich* by Napoleon Hill

- *Vision to Reality: How Short Term Massive Action Equals Long Term Maximum Results* by Honorée Corder

- *Finding Your Element: How to Discover Your Talents and Passions and Transform Your Life* by Sir Ken Robinson and Lou Aronica

ON DEVELOPING YOUR MONEY MINDSET

- *Think and Grow Rich* by Napoleon Hill

- *The Richest Man in Babylon* by George Samuel Clason

- *Rich Dad Poor Dad* by Robert Kiyosaki

- *Secrets of the Millionaire Mind: Mastering the Inner Game of Wealth* by T. Harv Ecker

- *The Total Money Makeover: A Proven Plan for Financial Fitness* by Dave Ramsey

- *The Millionaire Fastlane: Crack the Code to Wealth and Live Rich for a Lifetime* by MJ DeMarco

- *Profit First: A Simple System to Transform Any Business from a Cash-Eating Monster to a Money-Making Machine* by Mike Michalowicz

- *MONEY: Master the Game: 7 Simple Steps to Financial Freedom* by Tony Robbins

ON BEING A COLLEGE STUDENT

- *How to Become a Straight-A Student: The Unconventional Strategies Real College Students Use to Score High While Studying Less* by Cal Newport

- *The Last Lecture* by Randy Pausch

- *Debt-Free U* by Zac Bissonnette

- *10 Steps to Earning Awesome Grades (While Studying Less)* by Thomas Frank

- *Skating Through College: How to Pursue Your Passions and Make a Difference Without Sacrificing Your GPA* by John P Israel

- *Living College Life in the Front Row* by Jon Vroman

- *Do Your Laundry or You'll Die Alone: Advice Your Mom Would Give If She Thought You Were Listening* by Becky Blades

- *How to Win at College: Surprising Secrets for Success from the Country's Top Students* by Cal Newport

- *23 Anti-Procrastination Habits: How to Stop Being Lazy and Get Results You Want* by S. J. Scott

- *Why Didn't They Teach Me This in School?: 99 Personal Money Management Principles to Live By* by Cary Siegel

- *Born for This: How to Find the Work You Were Meant to Do* by Chris Guillebeau

- *You Are a Badass: How to Stop Doubting Your Greatness and Start Living an Awesome Life* by Jen Sincero

- *What the Best College Students Do* by Ken Bain

- *The Defining Decade: Why Your Twenties Matter—and How to Make the Most of Them Now* by Meg Jay

- *Life After College: The Complete Guide to Getting What You Want* by Jenny Blake

- *Never Pay Retail for College* by Beth W. Walker

MATH CONVERSION CHARTS

Length

1 centimeter	=	100 millimeters
1 meter	=	10,000 centimeters
1 hectare	=	10,000 meters
1 kilometer	=	100 hectares
1 kilometer	=	1 million meters
1 foot	=	144 inches
1 yard	=	9 feet
1 acre	=	4,840 yards
1 kilometer	=	100 hectares
1 kilometer	=	1 million meters

Weight

1 gram	=	1000 millograms
1 kilogram	=	1000 grams
1 ton	=	1 kilogram
1 pound	=	16 ounces
1 ton	=	2000 pounds

Volume

1 liter	=	1000 milliliters
1 tablespoon	=	3 teaspoons
1 cup	=	8 fluid ounces
1 pint	=	20 fluid ounces
1 quart	=	2 pints
1 gallon	=	4 quarts
1 gallon	=	8 pints
1 peck	=	2 gallons
1 bushel	=	2 pecks

US MAP

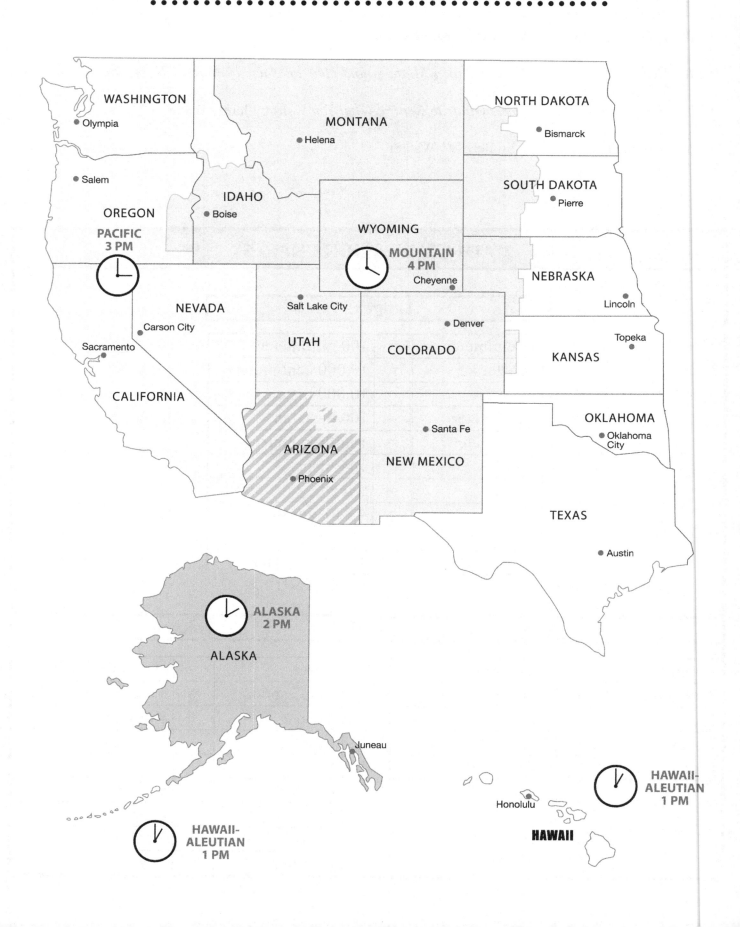

Capitols & Timezones

ABOUT THE AUTHORS

HAL ELROD is one of the highest-rated keynote speakers in America, as evidenced by his average of 9.7 out of 10.0 rating across multiple Entrepreneur Organization (EO) chapters. However, he's still best known as the author of what is now being widely regarded as one of the most life-changing books ever written (with 1,500+ five-star reviews on Amazon), *The Miracle Morning: The Not-So-Obvious Secret Guaranteed to Transform Your Life (Before 8AM)*, which has been translated into 21 languages and is a best seller around the world.

The seed for Hal's life's work was planted at age 20 when Hal was found dead at the scene of a horrific car accident. Hit head-on by a drunk driver at 70 miles per hour, he broke 11 bones, died for six minutes, and suffered permanent brain damage. After six days in a coma, he woke to face his unimaginable reality—which included being told by doctors that he would never walk again. Defying the logic of doctors, and proving that all of us are capable of overcoming even seemingly insurmountable adversity to achieve anything we set our minds to, Hal went on not only to walk again, but to run a 52-mile ultramarathon and become a hall of fame business achiever, international best-selling author, keynote speaker, and host of the *Achieve Your Goals* podcast on iTunes.

Most importantly, Hal is beyond grateful to now be married to the woman of his dreams and a father of two, sharing his life with his wife and children in Austin, Texas.

For more information on Hal's keynote speaking, live events, coaching, books, and the soon-to-be released *Miracle Morning Movie* (documentary), visit www.HalElrod.com.

NATALIE JANJI is a graduate of Loyola Marymount University and has a bachelor's degree in chemistry. After reading *The Miracle Morning* book, she became aware of her growing passion to help college students live to their full potential. Natalie is currently a speaker, coach, and author ready to set the world on fire (figuratively). You can find out more about her at NatalieJanji.com. Connect with her personally on Facebook.com/natalie.janji, **The Miracle Morning for College Students** Facebook page, Instagram @nat_janji, Twitter @janji_natalie, and LinkedIn, where you will find motivation, advice, and any help you would need when it comes to success in college and life.

HONORÉE CORDER is the author of dozens of books, including *You Must Write a Book, Vision to Reality, The Prosperous Writer* book series, *Business Dating, The Successful Single Mom* book series, *If Divorce is a Game, These are the Rules,* and *The Divorced Phoenix.* She is also Hal Elrod's business partner in *The Miracle Morning* book series. Honorée coaches business professionals, writers, and aspiring non-fiction authors who want to publish their books to bestseller status, create a platform, and develop multiple streams of income. She also does all sorts of other magical things, and her badassery is legendary. You can find out more at HonoreeCorder.com.

NOTES

NOTES

Made in the USA
Middletown, DE
24 April 2022

64576442R00199